GRADE

K

Implementing Investigations in Kindergarten

Infinity Prime Donna Casey

"This fractal is a classic spiral, which is my favorite, and I'm always amazed at the variations and the endlessly repeating patterns that can be created out of such a primary shape." – **Donna Casey**

Investigations

IN NUMBER, DATA, AND SPACE®

Power Polygons™ is a trademark of ETA/Cuisenaire®.

Use of the trademark or company name implies no relationship, sponsorship, endorsement, sale, or promotion on the part of Pearson Education, Inc., or its affiliates.

Glenview, Illinois • Boston, Massachusetts
Chandler, Arizona • Upper Saddle River, New Jersey

The Investigations Curriculum was developed by TERC, Cambridge, MA.

This material is based on work supported by the National Science Foundation ("NSF") under Grant No. ESI-0095450. Any opinions, findings, and conclusions or recommendations expressed in this material are those of the author(s) and do not necessarily reflect the views of the National Science Foundation.

ISBN-13: 978-0-328-60214-8

ISBN-10: 0-328-60214-0

3 4 5 6 7 8 9 10 V063 14 13 12

TERC

Co-Principal Investigators

Susan Jo Russell

Karen Economopoulos

Authors

Lucy Wittenberg
Director Grades 3–5

Karen Economopoulos
Director Grades K–2

Virginia Bastable
(SummerMath for Teachers,
Mt. Holyoke College)

Katie Hickey Bloomfield

Keith Cochran

Darrell Earnest

Arusha Hollister

Nancy Horowitz

Erin Leidl

Megan Murray

Young Oh

Beth W. Perry

Susan Jo Russell

Deborah Schifter
(Education
Development Center)

Kathy Sillman

Administrative Staff

Amy Taber
Project Manager

Beth Bergeron

Lorraine Brooks

Emi Fujiwara

Contributing Authors

Denise Baumann

Jennifer DiBrienza

Hollee Freeman

Paula Hooper

Jan Mokros

Stephen Monk
(University of Washington)

Mary Beth O'Connor

Judy Storeygard

Cornelia Tierney

Elizabeth Van Cleef

Carol Wright

Technology

Jim Hammerman

Classroom Field Work

Amy Appell

Rachel E. Davis

Traci Higgins

Julia Thompson

Note: Unless otherwise noted, all contributors listed above were staff of the Education Research Collaborative at TERC during their work on the curriculum. Other affiliations during the time of development are listed.

Collaborating Teachers

This group of dedicated teachers carried out extensive field testing in their classrooms, met regularly to discuss issues of teaching and learning mathematics, provided feedback to staff, welcomed staff into their classrooms to document students' work, and contributed both suggestions and written material that has been incorporated into the curriculum.

Bethany Altchek

Linda Amaral

Kimberly Beauregard

Barbara Bernard

Nancy Buell

Rose Christiansen

Chris Colbath-Hess

Lisette Colon

Kim Cook

Frances Cooper

Kathleen Drew

Rebeka Eston Salemi

Thomas Fisher

Michael Flynn

Holly Ghazey

Susan Gillis

Danielle Harrington

Elaine Herzog

Francine Hiller

Kirsten Lee Howard

Liliana Klass

Leslie Kramer

Melissa Lee Andrichak

Kelley Lee Sadowski

Jennifer Levitan

Mary Lou LoVecchio

Kristen McEnaney

Maura McGrail

Kathe Millett

Florence Molyneaux

Amy Monkiewicz

Elizabeth Monopoli

Carol Murray

Robyn Musser

Christine Norrman

Deborah O'Brien

Timothy O'Connor

Anne Marie O'Reilly

Mark Paige

Margaret Riddle

Karen Schweitzer

Elisabeth Seyferth

Susan Smith

Debra Sorvillo

Shoshanah Starr

Janice Szymaszek

Karen Tobin

JoAnn Trauschke

Ana Vaisenstein

Yvonne Watson

Michelle Woods

Mary Wright

Advisors

Deborah Lowenberg Ball,
University of Michigan

Hyman Bass, Professor of Mathematics and Mathematics Education
University of Michigan

Mary Canner, Principal, Natick Public Schools

Thomas Carpenter, Professor of Curriculum and Instruction,
University of Wisconsin–Madison

Janis Freckmann, Elementary Mathematics Coordinator,
Milwaukee Public Schools

Lynne Godfrey, Mathematics Coach,
Cambridge Public Schools

Ginger Hanlon, Instructional Specialist in Mathematics,
New York City Public Schools

DeAnn Huinker, Director, Center for Mathematics and
Science Education Research, University of Wisconsin–Milwaukee

James Kaput, Professor of Mathematics,
University of Massachusetts–Dartmouth

Kate Kline, Associate Professor, Department of Mathematics
and Statistics, Western Michigan University

Jim Lewis, Professor of Mathematics,
University of Nebraska–Lincoln

William McCallum, Professor of Mathematics,
University of Arizona

Harriet Pollatsek, Professor of Mathematics,
Mt. Holyoke College

Debra Shein-Gerson, Elementary Mathematics Specialist,
Weston Public Schools

Gary Shevell, Assistant Principal,
New York City Public Schools

Liz Sweeney, Elementary Math Department,
Boston Public Schools

Lucy West, Consultant,
Metamorphosis: Teaching Learning Communities, Inc.

This revision of the curriculum was built on the work of the many authors who contributed to the first edition (published between 1994 and 1998). We acknowledge the critical contributions of these authors in developing the content and pedagogy of *Investigations*:

Authors

Joan Akers

Michael T. Battista

Douglas H. Clements

Karen Economopoulos

Marlene Kliman

Jan Mokros

Megan Murray

Ricardo Nemirovsky

Andee Rubin

Susan Jo Russell

Cornelia Tierney

Contributing Authors

Mary Berle-Carman

Rebecca B. Corwin

Rebeka Eston

Claryce Evans

Anne Goodrow

Cliff Konold

Chris Mainhart

Sue McMillen

Jerrie Moffet

Tracy Noble

Kim O'Neil

Mark Ogonowski

Julie Sarama

Amy Shulman Weinberg

Margie Singer

Virginia Woolley

Tracey Wright

Contents

Contents

PART 1

Collaborating with the Authors

Goals and Guiding Principles

Investigations in Number, Data, and Space is a K–5 mathematics curriculum designed to engage students in making sense of mathematical ideas. Six major goals guided the development of this curriculum. The curriculum is designed to

- Support students to make sense of mathematics and learn that they can be mathematical thinkers.

- Focus on computational fluency with whole numbers as a major goal of the elementary grades.

- Provide substantive work in important areas of mathematics—rational numbers, geometry, measurement, data, and early algebra—and connections among them.

- Emphasize reasoning about mathematical ideas.

- Communicate mathematics content and pedagogy to teachers.

- Engage the range of learners in understanding mathematics.

Underlying these goals are three guiding principles that are touchstones for the *Investigations* team as we approach both students and teachers as agents of their own learning:

1. *Students have mathematical ideas.* Students come to school with ideas about numbers, shapes, measurements, patterns, and data. If given the opportunity to learn in an environment that stresses making sense of mathematics, students build on the ideas they already have and learn about new mathematics they have never encountered. They learn mathematical content and develop fluency and skill that is well grounded in meaning. Students learn that they are capable of having mathematical ideas, applying what they know to new situations, and thinking and reasoning about unfamiliar problems.

2. *Teachers are engaged in ongoing learning* about mathematics content, pedagogy, and student learning. The curriculum provides material for professional development, to be used by teachers individually or in groups, that supports teachers' continued learning as they use the curriculum over several years. The *Investigations* curriculum materials are designed as much to be a dialogue with teachers as to be a core of content for students.

3. *Teachers collaborate with the students and curriculum materials* to create the curriculum as enacted in the classroom. The only way for a good curriculum to be used well is for teachers to be active participants in implementing it. Teachers use the curriculum to maintain a clear, focused, and coherent agenda for mathematics teaching. At the same time, they observe and listen carefully to students, try to understand how they are thinking, and make teaching decisions based on these observations.

The Teacher-Student-Curriculum Partnership

Mathematics teaching and learning at its best is a collaboration among teachers, students, and the curriculum. Both the teacher and the curriculum contribute to this partnership in important ways. The curriculum materials provide a coherent, carefully sequenced core of mathematics content for students and supportive professional development material for teachers. Teachers are active partners in learning the curriculum well, understanding how each mathematical focus is developed, and implementing the curriculum in a way that accommodates the needs of their particular students.

The *Investigations* curriculum was field-tested in many different classrooms, representing a range of students and teachers, over several years. Thousands of hours of classroom observation, documentation, analysis of student work, and meetings with teachers were involved. Activities and the way they are presented to students were revised again and again.

Each time a curriculum unit was tested in a classroom, no matter how many times it had been tried and revised before, there was always more to discover about how students learn and how activities can be revised and modified to support them. This process, we have come to believe, can be endless. Just as you, a classroom teacher, learn more about students' learning each year, so do those of us who develop the curriculum. At some point we decide that, considering all the evidence, the curriculum has been sufficiently tested and works well for a wide range of students.

This lengthy and detailed process has resulted in a coherent core curriculum that is based on the real needs of real students and teachers. The process has also provided ample evidence that the collaboration of the teacher is essential. Only the teacher can understand and support the particular learning needs of a particular class of students in a particular school year. Only the teacher is present every day in the classroom, observing students' work, listening to their discourse, and developing an understanding of their mathematical ideas by analyzing what they say and do. In mathematics, as in any subject, only the teacher can continually assess students' strengths and needs and think through how best to accommodate differences to involve all students in substantive and challenging work.

How *Investigations* Supports the Teacher's Role

Modifying the curriculum and making it work in your classroom requires knowing the curriculum well. It means taking the time to understand the mathematics focus of each lesson and how the mathematical ideas build over many lessons. Learning the curriculum well means holding back the urge to change activities because you think they are too easy or too difficult for your students before you have tried them and actually seen your students' work. Keep in mind that the way ideas are developed and sequenced has been researched and tested in multiple classrooms, and many suggestions for accommodations are already built into the

curriculum. Teachers tell us that they generally follow the curriculum as it is written the first year, and that they learn a great deal when activities that they thought would not work with their students turn out to be crucial to student learning.

You are an active partner in this teacher-student-curriculum partnership, and the curriculum must support your complex job by providing information about mathematics content and student learning. From the beginning, our intention in developing *Investigations* has been to create a professional development tool for teachers—a tool that provides opportunities for learning about mathematics content, how students learn, and effective pedagogy. Our design focuses as much on the teacher as learner as on the student as learner.

Two sections at the beginning of each curriculum unit, Mathematics in This Unit and Assessment in This Unit, provide an overview of the mathematics content, Math Focus Points, and benchmarks for student learning. The Math Focus Points for each session and the assessment benchmarks tell the mathematical story line of each curriculum unit so that you can productively guide students' work. Math Focus Points make explicit the purposes of the activities in each session and help you make choices about how to guide discussions. The assessment benchmarks for each curriculum unit are an aid in determining priorities and interpreting students' work.

The "teacher talk" printed in blue in each session is also an aid for focusing an activity and choosing questions to ask. It is not a script for how to address your students; it is a guide based on classroom experience with different ways of talking about mathematical ideas, introducing activities, and asking effective questions.

Teacher Notes collected at the end of each curriculum unit focus on key mathematical ideas and how students learn them. Because having students reason about, articulate, and justify their ideas is such a central part of the curriculum, Dialogue Boxes provide examples of student discussion and teachers' efforts to focus this discussion. Additionally, examples of what students might say in class appear within the session descriptions.

To further support your work with the curriculum, this *Implementing Investigations in Kindergarten* book provides an overview of the math content for the entire year (Part 3), a set of Teacher Notes that applies to the curriculum as a whole (Part 6), and a set of classroom cases written by teachers that provides examples of how they work with the range of learners in their classrooms (Part 7).

Teachers who use the *Investigations* curriculum over several years find that, as they teach a curriculum unit more than once, they gradually read more and more of the supporting material and incorporate it into their work with students. Teachers also use features such as the Teacher Notes and Dialogue Boxes as part of grade-level study groups or within other professional development structures. The better you know the curriculum and your students, the more you can internalize the mathematics focus and sequence and the better decisions you can make to support your students' learning.

PART 2

Using *Investigations*

Components of the Program

Curriculum Units

The curriculum at each grade level is organized into nine units (seven for Kindergarten). These curriculum units are your teaching guides for the program. The unit organization is further described in the next section, "Using the Curriculum Units."

Each curriculum unit in Kindergarten offers from $3\frac{1}{2}$ to 5 weeks of work, and focuses on the area of mathematics identified in the unit's subtitle.

This pacing is based on a school year that starts in early September, ends in late June, and has vacation weeks in February and April. The pacing will vary according to school calendars but may also vary depending on the needs of students, the school's years of experience with this curriculum, and other local factors.

Kindergarten Curriculum Units

Unit	Title	Number of Sessions	Suggested Pacing
1	**Who Is in School Today?** Classroom Routines and Materials	18	September–early October
2	**Counting and Comparing** Measurement and the Number System 1	24	Early October–November
3	**What Comes Next?** Patterns and Functions	22	November–December
4	**Measuring and Counting** Measurement and the Number System 2	26	December–January
5	**Make a Shape, Build a Block** 2-D and 3-D Geometry	20	February–March
6	**How Many Do You Have?** Addition, Subtraction, and the Number System	26	March–April
7	**Sorting and Surveys** Data Analysis	17	May–June

The curriculum units are designed for use in the sequence shown. Each succeeding unit builds on the previous unit, both within and across strands. For example, the three units that focus on the number system (Units 2, 4, and 6) develop a sequence of ideas across the three units. These ideas are built on throughout the Kindergarten curriculum, for example, as students determine the number of objects in the Counting Jar (all units); figure out the total number of repeating units in a repeating pattern in Unit 3 (Patterns and Functions); and as they collect, count, and represent data in Unit 7 (Data Analysis).

Resource Masters

Each Resource Masters CD contains the reproducible materials needed for classroom instruction. The use of all these materials for particular Investigations is specified in the curriculum units.

Investigations Software

Shapes Software for Kindergarten provides an environment in which students investigate a variety of geometric ideas, including relationships between shapes; how shapes combine to make other shapes; symmetry; and geometric transformations such as rotations (turns), translations (slides), and reflections (flips). This software is provided as a disk to be used with Unit 5, *Make a Shape, Build a Block,* and is also available through the Pearson website.

Investigations for the Interactive Whiteboard

Each grade has whole-class instructional support that enhances the session's content as well as the daily Classroom Routines.

Student Activity Book

A booklet accompanying the entire curriculum for Kindergarten contains the consumable pages for student work, including in-class work, game recording sheets, and all pages for daily practice and for homework.

Student Math Handbook Flip Chart

This flip chart offers a valuable reference to the math words and ideas introduced in the curriculum units, as well as visual prompts for repeating activities.

Manipulatives Kit

A kit of materials is coordinated with the activities and games at each grade level. The Kindergarten kit includes class sets of the following items:

Connecting cubes

Pattern blocks

Attribute blocks

Geoblocks

Wooden geometric solids

Geoboards with rubber bands

Buttons

Pennies

Color tiles

Two-color counters

Craft sticks

Teddy bear counters

Blank cubes and labels

Dot cubes

Number cubes

Monthly calendar with removable numbers

100 chart

Class number line

Cards in Card Kit

Manufactured cards are used with some of the activities and games at each grade level. The cards for Kindergarten are as follows:

Arrow Cards for the Pocket Chart

Attribute Cards

Car Cards

Primary Number Cards

Question Mark Cards

Ten-Frames

Implementing *Investigations* in Kindergarten

At each grade level, this guide to implementing *Investigations* includes an overview of the curriculum; suggestions for using the curriculum units in your classroom; a closer look at the mathematics content of that particular grade, including lists of the Math Focus Points for each curriculum unit; program-wide Teacher Notes that explain some key ideas underlying the curriculum; and a set of case studies about working with a range of learners that can be used for professional development.

The Curriculum Units

The curriculum unit is your main teaching tool. It is your blueprint for the sequence and purpose of the daily lessons; it also contains guidelines for assessment, suggestions for differentiating instruction, and professional development materials to support your teaching.

Structure of a Curriculum Unit

Each curriculum unit is divided into Investigations. An Investigation focuses on a set of related mathematical ideas, coordinating students' work in hands-on activities, written activities, and class discussions over a period of several days.

Investigations are divided into 30- to 45-minute sessions, or lessons. Sessions include the following features:

- *Math Focus Points:* This list of what students will be doing mathematically highlights the goals of each session.

- *Activities:* A session contains from one to three activities, organized as work for the whole class, pairs, small groups, or individuals.

- *Discussion:* Many sessions include whole-class time during which students compare methods and results and share conclusions. A subset of the session's Focus Points helps you guide each discussion.

- *Math Workshop:* In some sessions, students work in a Math Workshop format. Individually, in pairs, or in small groups, they choose from and cycle through a set of related activities. This setup is further discussed in a later section, "All About Math Workshop" (pp. 12–14).

- *Assessment:* Students are assessed through both written activities and observations; see "Assessment in this Unit" for further information.

- *Session Follow-up:* Homework is occasionally provided in Kindergarten. Each Investigation includes a page for Daily Practice. These pages offer directed practice of content in the current curriculum unit. They can be used either for additional homework or for in-class practice. Relevant pages in the *Student Math Handbook Flip Chart* are also referenced here.

Your Math Day

The *Investigations* curriculum assumes that you spend 30–45 minutes of each classroom day on mathematics, in addition to conducting brief Classroom Routines (further described later in this section and in Part 4 of this book). A chart called Today's Plan appears at the beginning of each session, laying out the suggested pacing for the activities in that 30- to 45-minute session. While you may need to adapt this structure to your particular classroom needs, be aware that it is important to move through all the activities because they are carefully designed to offer continued work on the key mathematical ideas. It is also essential that you allow time for class discussions, where students have an opportunity to articulate their own ideas, compare solutions, and consolidate understanding. See Teacher Note: Discussing Mathematical Ideas, on pages 52–54, for further information on the importance of these class discussions.

Differentiated Instruction

Within the sessions, you will regularly see a feature titled "Differentiation: Supporting the Range of Learners." This feature offers ideas for intervention or extensions related to the particular work of that session. Ideas for helping English Language Learners are offered at the beginning of the curriculum unit and where applicable in the sessions. In addition, Part 7 of this book, "Working with the Range of Learners: Classroom Cases," presents situations from actual *Investigations* classrooms and invites you to consider how these case studies can inform your own teaching practice.

Classroom Routines

These brief activities, described in a box below Today's Plan for each session, require about 10 minutes of additional daily work outside of math time. These routines, an important part of the *Investigations* curriculum, offer ongoing skill building, practice, and review that support the regular math work. They also reinforce work students have done in previous units; and help students increase their repertoire of strategies for mental calculation and problem solving. Part 4 of this book, "Classroom Routines," provides detailed explanations of the activities to plan for Kindergarten.

Assessment in This Unit

Opportunities for assessment are carefully woven throughout the curriculum units at each grade level. A section at the beginning of each curriculum unit identifies the benchmarks students will be expected to meet and specifies key activities you can observe, as well as the particular assessment activities where students will produce written work for your review. In Kindergarten, checklists are provided for each benchmark and are used for taking notes about what students understand as they engage in activities. As the last session of the curriculum unit approaches, teachers should look over the checklists to determine who has not yet met the benchmarks. While other students participate in a Math Workshop, the teacher then meets individually with those students to do one or more tasks during the End-of-Unit Assessment Session. Teacher Notes provide information about the mathematics of each benchmark, and Assessment Teacher Notes present a teacher's observations of her students while at work on the relevant activity or activities.

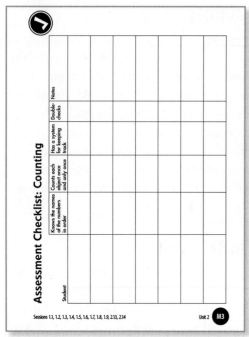

Assessment Checklist: Counting

Student	Knows the names of the numbers in order	Counts each object once and only once	Has a system for keeping track	Double-checks	Notes

Sessions 1.1, 1.2, 1.3, 1.4, 1.5, 1.6, 1.7, 1.8, 1.9, 2.13, 2.14   Unit 2 M3

▲ **An example of an Assessment Checklist**

"Ongoing Assessment: Observing Students at Work" is a regular feature of the sessions. It identifies the particular math focus and lists questions for you to consider as you observe your students solving problems, playing math games, and working on activities. Teacher observations are an important part of ongoing assessment. Although individual observations may be little more than snapshots of a student's experience with a single activity, when considered together over time, they can provide an informative and detailed picture. These observations can be useful in documenting and assessing a student's growth and offer important sources of information when preparing for family conferences or writing student reports.

You may want to develop a system to record and keep track of your observations of students. The most important aspect of a record-keeping system is that it be both manageable and useful for you. Some teachers use systems such as the following:

- Jot down observations of students' work on a class list of names. Because the space is somewhat limited, it is not possible to write lengthy notes; however, when kept over time, these short observations provide important information.

- Place stick-on address labels on a clipboard. Take notes on individual students and then peel these labels off and put them in a file for each student.

- Jot down brief notes at the end of each week. Some teachers find that this is a useful way of reflecting on the class as a whole, on the curriculum, and on individual students. Planning for the next week's activities can benefit from these weekly reflections.

Observation checklists, student work on written assessments, and other examples of students' written work can be collected in a portfolio. Suggestions for particular work that might be saved in a portfolio are listed at the beginning of each curriculum unit, under "Assessment in This Unit."

Professional Development

One guiding principle of the *Investigations* curriculum is to provide support that helps teachers improve their own understanding of the mathematics that they are teaching and the learning that they observe in their students. To this end, the following materials are included in the curriculum for teachers' professional development:

- *Mathematics in This Unit:* An essay at the beginning of each unit explains in detail the Mathematical Emphases of the unit, the Math Focus Points related to each area of emphasis, and the work students will be doing in each area.

- *Algebra Connections in This Unit:* This essay, appearing in each of the number and operations units and in the patterns, functions, and change units, explains how the activities and ideas of the unit are laying a foundation for students' later work with algebra.

- *Math Notes, Teaching Notes, and Algebra Notes:* Found in the margins of the sessions, these brief notes provide information about mathematics content or student thinking, as well as teaching tips to help teachers better understand the work of that session.

- *Teacher Notes:* These essays, collected at the end of each curriculum unit, provide further practical information about the mathematics content and how students learn it. Many of the notes were written in response to questions from teachers or to discuss important issues that arose in field-test classrooms. They offer teachers help with thinking about mathematical ideas that may be unfamiliar to them; they also provide guidance for observing and assessing students' work.

- *Dialogue Boxes:* Also at the end of each curriculum unit are Dialogue Boxes that reflect classroom scenarios related to the activities of the unit. Since these Dialogue Boxes are based on actual teacher-student interactions, you learn how students typically express their mathematical ideas, what issues and confusions arise in their thinking, and how some teachers have chosen to guide particular class discussions.

Working with Families

Families are important partners with schools in the process of teaching mathematics. Because the teaching of mathematics has been evolving, many families may be unfamiliar with the approaches taken by the *Investigations* curriculum. For this reason, a number of Family Letters are provided. In Kindergarten, these letters include the following:

- The first Family Letter in each curriculum unit, About the Mathematics in This Unit, introduces families to the mathematics that their children will be doing and to the benchmarks for that unit.

- A second letter in each curriculum unit, Related Activities to Try at Home, is sent home some time after the first. It suggests related activities that families can do together and children's books that support students' work in mathematics.

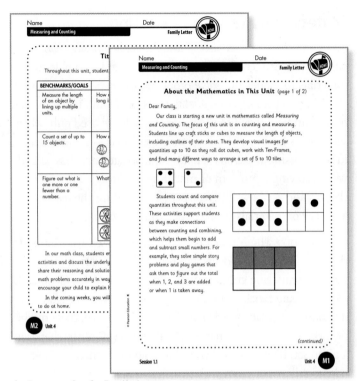

▲ An example of a Family Letter

Setting Up the *Investigations* Classroom

As you begin using the *Investigations* curriculum, you may find yourself making decisions about how to set up the tables and chairs in your classroom and where to keep your materials. Students will at various times need to work individually, in pairs or small groups, and as a whole class. When working in pairs or small groups, they need to be able to see one another's work and listen to one another's ideas. Bringing students together for whole-group discussion is also a regular feature of the curriculum, and during these discussions it is important that students can easily see and hear one another. Ways of making this work are further discussed in the Teacher Note: Discussing Mathematical Ideas, pages 52–54. You must also find ways to make materials and games easily accessible and consider how to organize the room for Math Workshops.

Materials as Tools for Learning

Tools and materials are used throughout the *Investigations* curriculum. Students of all ages benefit from being able to use materials to model and solve problems and explain their thinking. Encourage all students to use tools and materials and to explain how they use them. If materials are used only when someone is having difficulty, students can get the mistaken idea that using materials is a less sophisticated and less valued way of solving a problem or modeling a solution. Therefore, they should see how different people, including the teacher, use a variety of materials to solve the same problem.

Get to Know the Materials Familiarize yourself with some of the main materials students will use. In Kindergarten these include connecting cubes, pattern blocks, Geoblocks, Geoboards, and Attribute Blocks. In some units there are Teacher Notes that describe particular materials in detail. For example, these might provide the names and mathematical definitions of the shapes in a given set, illustrations of each shape, and information about how to talk about them with students.

Storing Materials Many of the *Investigations* materials come in large containers. Split these sets into smaller, equivalent subsets and store each in a clear container or shoe box, labeled with the name and a picture of the material. Include a small cup to use as a scoop. Store materials where they are easily accessible to students, perhaps on a bookshelf or along a windowsill. In addition to pattern blocks, Geoblocks, and connecting cubes, assorted counters and paper (blank and grid) are important mathematical tools that should be available to students. Individual units also provide suggestions on preparing some materials for classroom use.

Introducing a New Material Students need time to explore a new material before using it in structured activities. By freely exploring a material, students will discover many of its important characteristics and will have some understanding of when it might make sense to use it. Although some free exploration is built into regular math time, many teachers make materials available to students during free time or before or after school.

Plan How Students Will Use Materials The more available materials are, the more likely students are to use them. Having materials available means that they are readily accessible and that students are allowed to make decisions about which tools to use and when and how to use them. In much the same way that you choose the best tool to use for certain projects or tasks, students also should be encouraged to think about which material best meets their needs. Initially you may need to place materials close to students as they work. Gradually students should be expected to decide what they need and get materials on their own.

In order to make such a system work, you will need to establish clear expectations about how materials will be used and cared for.

- **Sharing Materials.** Even though a scoop should guarantee an ample assortment and quantity of materials, students might not get the exact piece they desire. Conversations about sharing are critical.

- **Using Materials Appropriately.** Rules and policies for the appropriate use of materials should be established at the beginning of the year. This might include things such as not throwing the materials, not drawing on them, and so on. Consider asking the students to suggest rules for how materials should and should not be used. Students are often more attentive to rules and policies that they have helped create.

- **Cleaning Up Materials.** Making an announcement a few minutes before the end of a work time helps prepare students for the transition that is about to occur. You can then give students several minutes to return materials to their containers and shelves and to double-check the floor for any stray materials.

Games in the *Investigations* Curriculum

The games included in this curriculum are a central part of the mathematics in each curriculum unit, not just enrichment activities. Games are used to develop concepts and to practice skills, such as learning to count and compare quantities, learning to sort and classify objects, finding different combinations that make a number, or sequencing numbers. The rationale for using games is as follows:

- Games provide engaging opportunities for students to deepen their understanding of numbers and operations and to practice computation.

- Playing games encourages strategic mathematical thinking as students find an optimal way (rather than just any way) of "winning" the game.

- Games provide repeated practice without requiring the teacher to provide new problems.

- While students are playing the games, the teacher is free to observe students or to work with individuals or small groups.

Before introducing a game to students, it is important that you play the game yourself or with colleagues. By doing so you will learn the rules of the game, explore the mathematical ideas that students will encounter as they play, and figure out the materials needed for the game. This will also help you determine the preparation needed (for instance, cutting out cards, gathering other materials, making "game packs") and helps you decide the best way to introduce the game to your students (pre-teaching it to some students, small or whole group introduction, etc.). For some games, variations are offered. Before using these variations, or any

others you might think of, consider how changing the rules of the game changes the mathematical ideas with which students are working.

Because students find them engaging, games are an excellent vehicle for providing repeated practice, without the need for the teacher to provide new problems. Therefore, students play games repeatedly, over time, throughout the *Investigations* curriculum. The more students play, the better. Therefore, some teachers encourage students to play games at other times as well: in the morning as students arrive, during indoor recess, as choices when other work is finished, and for homework. Consider making "game packs" for such times by placing the directions and needed materials in resealable plastic bags. Students can check them out during free times or take them home to play with a family member.

▲ **An example of a game recording sheet**

All About Math Workshop

Math Workshop provides an opportunity for students to work on a variety of activities that usually focus on similar mathematical content. The activities are not sequential; as students move among them, they continually revisit the important concepts and ideas they are learning. By repeatedly playing a game, or solving similar problems, students are able to refine strategies, use different contexts, and bring new knowledge to familiar experiences. Math Workshop is designed to

- Provide students with repeated experience with the concepts being learned and time to practice important skills and refine strategies.

- Provide time for the teacher to work with individuals and small groups and to assess students' learning and understanding.

- Help students develop independence and learn to take responsibility for their own learning as they choose activities, keep track of their work, use and take care of classroom materials, and work with others.

It is important to structure Math Workshop in ways that work for you and your students. The following questions can guide decision-making about how to set up Math Workshop in your classroom. You may need to experiment before finding the way that works best for you and your students.

How should the activities be organized? How will the materials be made available?

Some teachers set activities up at centers or stations around the room. At each center students find the materials needed to complete the activity. Others store materials in a central location and have students bring materials to their desks or tables. In either case, materials should be readily accessible to students, and students should be expected to take responsibility for cleaning up and returning materials to their appropriate storage locations. Giving students a "five minutes until cleanup" warning before the end of an activity session allows them to finish what they are working on and prepare for the upcoming transition.

How do I decide how many students can work on an activity at once?

Most teachers limit the number of students who work on a Math Workshop activity at one time. Because students often want to do a new activity immediately after it is introduced, you will need to reassure them that everyone will have repeated chances to do each activity. In many cases, the quantity of materials available limits the number of students who can do an activity at any one time. Even if this is not the case, set guidelines about the number of students that work on each choice. This gives students the opportunity to work in smaller groups and to make decisions about what they want and need to do. It also provides a chance to do visit activities repeatedly.

How will the class know what the activities are, and how many students can work on an activity at once?

Primary teachers have different ways of communicating such information to students. For example, some list the activities on the board, on the overhead, or on a piece of chart paper and sketch a picture next to each to help students who cannot yet read the activity names. Others use a pocket chart or laminate a piece of tag-board to create a Math Workshop board that they can easily update as new activities are added from session to session and old activities are no longer offered.

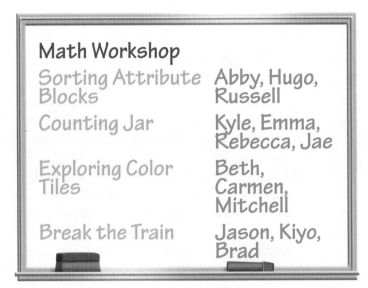

Math Workshop

Sorting Attribute Blocks	Abby, Hugo, Russell
Counting Jar	Kyle, Emma, Rebecca, Jae
Exploring Color Tiles	Beth, Carmen, Mitchell
Break the Train	Jason, Kiyo, Brad

Some teachers label each activity with a number, or with drawings of stick figures, to show how many students can do the activity at once. Others explain that the number of chairs at a particular table or station show how many students it can accommodate.

How do I help students make choices about the activities they will do and use their time productively?

Initially you may need to help students plan what they do when. Support students in making decisions about the activities they do, rather than organizing students into groups and circulating the groups every fifteen minutes or making Math Workshops whole class activities. Making choices, planning their time, and taking responsibility for their own learning are important aspects of students' school experiences. If some students return to the same activity over and over again without trying others, suggest that they make a different first choice and then do the favorite activity as a second choice. Other students may need to be encouraged to use their time efficiently to complete all activities.

In any classroom there will be a range of how much work students can complete. Making Math Workshop activities available at other times during the day allows students to revisit favorite activities; gives students who need it more time to finish their work; and can provide targeted practice for all students. Many Math Workshop activities include extensions and/or additional problems for students to do when they have completed their required work. You can also encourage students to return to activities they have done before, solve another problem or two, or play a game again.

How do I keep track, and help students keep track, of the activities they have completed and the work they have done?

Some teachers design a Math Workshop board that keeps track of which activities students are choosing. Some use a class list to jot notes as students make choices at the beginning of each Math Workshop. Others ask students to record the name and/or a picture of the activity on a blank sheet of paper when they have finished. Still others post a sheet for each activity—with the name and the corresponding picture—at the front of the room or at each station. When students have completed an activity, they print their name on the corresponding sheet.

Whenever students do work on paper during Math Workshop, you should handle this as you do any other completed or yet-to-be finished math work (e.g., a math folder, binder, desk, cubby, etc.). Keeping a date stamp at the front of the room (or at each Math Workshop station), makes it easy for students to record the date, which can also help you keep track of their work.

How do I help students work independently, cooperatively, and productively?

As you introduce Math Workshop, and as students experience it over time, it is critical to establish clear guidelines and to clearly communicate your expectations. Be sure to describe and discuss students' responsibilities:

• Be productively engaged during Math Workshop.

• Work on every activity [at least once].

• If you don't understand or feel stuck, [ask a friend]. (Some teachers establish an "ask three, then me" rule, requiring students to check with three peers before coming to the teacher for help.)

Plan to spend a few minutes at the end of Math Workshop, particularly early in the year, discussing what went smoothly, what sorts of issues arose and how they were resolved, and what students enjoyed or found difficult. Having students share the work they have been doing often sparks interest in an activity. Some days, you might ask two or three volunteers to talk about their work. On other days, you might pose a question that someone asked you during Math Workshop, so that other students might respond to it. Encourage students to be involved in the process of finding solutions to problems that come up in the classroom. In doing so, they take some responsibility for their own behavior and become involved with establishing classroom policies.

What should I be doing during Math Workshop?

Initially, much of your time during Math Workshop will be spent circulating around the classroom, helping students get settled into activities, monitoring the process of moving from one choice to another, and generally managing the classroom. Once routines are familiar and well established, students will become more independent and responsible for their work during Math Workshop. This will allow you to spend more concentrated periods of time observing the class as a whole or working with individuals and small groups.

Once Math Workshop is running smoothly, this structure provides you with the opportunity to observe and listen to students while they work. Because students are working on different activities at the same time, you can structure and adapt activities to fit their varying needs. Also, you can meet with individual students, pairs, or small groups who need help or more challenge, or whom you haven't had a chance to observe before, or to do individual assessments. Recording your observations of students will help you keep track of how they are interacting with materials and solving problems. See *Assessment in This Unit* (pp. 7–8), which offers some strategies for recording and using observations of students.

PART 3

Mathematics in Kindergarten

Number and Operations: Whole Numbers

Counting and the Number System

A main focus in Kindergarten is counting, which is the basis for understanding the number system and for almost all the number work in the primary grades. Students hear and use the counting sequence (the number names, in order) in a variety of contexts. They have many opportunities to connect the number names with the written numbers and with the quantities they represent. They have repeated experiences counting sets of objects, along with matching and making sets of a given size. As students count sets of objects and make equal sets, they begin to see the importance of counting each object once and only once and of having a system for keeping track of what has been counted and what still remains to be counted. Students engage in repeated practice with counting and develop visual images for quantities up to 10.

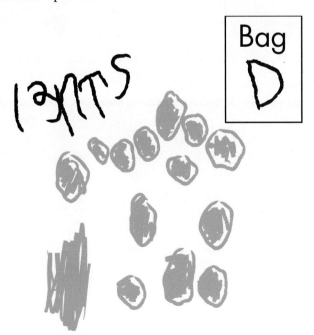

▲ This student used pictures, numbers, and words to show that he counted 13 nuts. He drew a circle for each nut and wrote both the number and the word—"13 nts." When he recounted his circles to check, he realized he had one too many, so he scribbled out one circle.

As students are developing accurate counting strategies, they are also building an understanding of how numbers in the counting sequence are related: Each number is one more (or one less) than the number before (or after) it. Students develop an understanding of the concepts of greater than, fewer than, and equal to and develop language for describing quantitative comparisons (e.g., bigger, more, smaller, fewer, less, same, equal) as they count and compare quantities.

Example: Write the names of people in your home. Circle the name with the most letters.

Daniel   Matt   (Kaitlyn)

Sara   Mom   Dad

Mathematical Emphases

Counting and Quantity

- Developing strategies for accurately counting a set of objects by ones

- Developing an understanding of the magnitude and position of numbers

- Developing the idea of equivalence

Benchmarks (Compiled from Units 2, 4, and 6)

- Count a set of up to 10 objects.

- Compare two quantities up to 10 to see which is greater.

- Count a set of up to 15 objects.

- Figure out what is one more or one fewer than a number.

- Write the numbers up to 10.

- Count a set of up to 20 objects.

Addition and Subtraction

Young students develop their understanding of addition and subtraction by having many opportunities to count, visualize, model, solve, and discuss different types of problems. Many of the counting activities in Kindergarten build a bridge to the operations of addition and subtraction, as students add a small amount to a set or remove a small amount from a set and figure out "How many now?" One of the ways students are introduced to addition and subtraction is via story problems about combining and separating. They retell the stories, act them out, and solve them by modeling the action involved and using counting strategies. Students also play a variety of games that model both addition and subtraction. They have repeated experiences joining two or more amounts and removing an amount from a whole.

Later in the year, students work with combinations of quantities that they can count fluently. As they find ways to arrange and describe sets of 5–10 square tiles or record combinations of two-color counters, they begin to see that numbers can be composed in different ways. They work on activities that involve seeing and describing a given quantity (e.g., 6 tiles) as made up of groups (e.g., a group of 4 and a group of 2). They are also asked to decompose quantities (e.g., 6 can be split into 4 and 2) and to find one or more combinations for a quantity (e.g., 6 can also be decomposed as 6 and 0, 3 and 3, or 5 and 1). This work lays the foundation for making meaningful sense of $4 + 2 = 6$ and $6 - 4 = 2$ in subsequent grades.

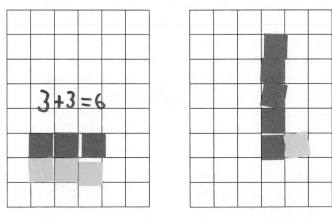

Students record their arrangements of six tiles and indicate how they know there are six tiles in all.

Name RAUL Date

Measuring and Counting

One More, One Fewer

Starting Number	+1 or −1	Ending Total
3	(+1) / −1	4
2	+1 / (−1)	1
5	(+1) / −1	6
4	(+1) / −1	5
3	+1 / (−1)	2
7	(+1) / −1	8
9	(+1) / −1	10

Sessions 3.3, 3.4, 3.5, 3.6, 3.7   Unit 4 **M21**

▲ Sample student work from the activity
One More, One Fewer

Example: Record the total number of chips. Toss the chips. Record the number that are red and the number that are yellow.

Total Number: __6__

●	●
Red	Yellow
2	4
5	1
3	3
3	3
4	2

Students use mathematical tools and representations to model and solve problems to clarify and communicate their thinking. Kindergartners are just beginning to learn how to represent their mathematical work on paper and are encouraged to do so in ways that make sense to them. Many use combinations of pictures, words, and numbers.

Mathematical Emphases

Whole Number Operations

• Making sense of and developing strategies to solve addition and subtraction problems with small numbers

• Using manipulatives, drawings, tools, and notation to show strategies and solutions

Benchmark

• Combine two small quantities.

Measurement

In Kindergarten, students are introduced to length and linear measurement through measuring by direct comparison. As they compare several objects to determine the longest object, they discuss and make sense of important aspects of accurate measurement, such as choosing which dimension to measure.

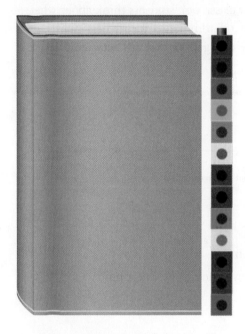

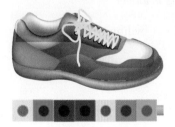

Students begin to think about the different dimensions of objects.

They also hear, become comfortable with, and use language to describe length—long, short, wide, tall, high (and their comparative forms—longer, wider, etc.). Later in the year, students use multiple nonstandard units (e.g., craft sticks or cubes) to quantify length: "How many craft sticks long is this desk? the path from the window to the door?" "How many cubes long is my shoe? this pencil?" As they measure lengths around their classroom, students think about what happens if the nonstandard units are (or are not) laid straight or if there are (or are not) gaps or overlaps between them.

Students begin to think about measuring accurately.

Mathematical Emphasis

Linear Measurement

• Understanding length and using linear units

Benchmarks

• Decide which of two objects is longer.

• Measure the length of an object by lining up multiple units.

Geometry

The geometry work in Kindergarten builds on students' firsthand knowledge of shapes to further develop their spatial sense and deepen their understanding of the two-dimensional (2-D) and three-dimensional (3-D) world in which they live. As students identify the different shapes that make up the world, they are encouraged to use their own words to describe both 2-D and 3-D shapes. In this way, they form images of familiar shapes by associating them with familiar objects.

Students explore the geometric idea that shapes can be combined or subdivided to make other shapes. For example, they investigate how 3-D shapes can be combined to form a particular rectangular prism.

Different types of blocks can be combined to form the same rectangular prism.

By putting shapes together and taking shapes apart, students deepen their understanding of the attributes of shapes and how shapes are related.

Students also construct 2-D and 3-D shapes with clay and on Geoboards. As they construct shapes, they form mental images of the shapes and think about the attributes of particular shapes.

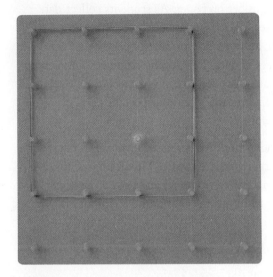

▲ Students construct shapes on Geoboards.

The *Shapes* Software is introduced as a tool for extending and deepening this work. This tool is designed for K–2 students to explore how different shapes can be combined to form other shapes, experiment with different types of geometric transformations (rotation, translation, reflection), make patterns, and investigate symmetry.

Mathematical Emphases

Features of Shape

- Composing and decomposing 2-D and 3-D shapes

- Describing, identifying, comparing, and sorting 2-D and 3-D shapes

Benchmarks

- Describe the overall size, shape, function, and/or features of familiar 2-D and 3-D shapes.

- Construct 2-D and 3-D shapes.

- Make 2-D and 3-D shapes by combining shapes.

Patterns and Functions

Kindergarten students construct, describe, extend, and determine what comes next in repeating patterns. To identify and construct repeating patterns, students must be able to identify the attributes of the objects in the pattern. Therefore, students first work on sorting objects by their attributes, before they begin to construct their own patterns. Students encounter repeating patterns with two (AB, AAB, ABB) or three (ABC) elements. As students construct and describe many different patterns, they become more familiar with the structure of patterns, are able to identify what comes next in a pattern, and can begin to think about how two patterns are similar and different.

Example: What is the same about these cube trains? What is different?

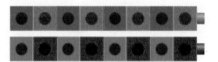

After having many opportunities to construct their own patterns and extend patterns made by others, students begin to analyze the structure of a repeating pattern by identifying the *unit* of the pattern—the part of the pattern that repeats over and over.

Example: What is the repeating unit of this pattern?

Mathematical Emphases

Repeating Patterns

- Constructing, describing, and extending repeating patterns

- Identifying the unit of a repeating pattern

Benchmarks

- Copy, construct, and extend simple repeating patterns, such as AB and ABC.

- Begin to identify the unit of a repeating pattern.

Data Analysis

Sorting and classifying are central to organizing and interpreting data. Kindergarten students have many opportunities to identify the attributes of groups of objects, determine how the objects are the same and different, and sort them into groups according to their attributes. Students apply these skills to organizing data when they sort their favorite lunch foods into categories.

What We Like for Lunch

fruit · vegetables · things you drink · things with bread · cookies and cake

One way students sorted their lunch data.

Students think about how these pieces of information are the same and different when determining how the data might be grouped and how those groups can be defined.

Important to any data collection activity is the need to establish the group of people or objects being considered. Students begin their work on data by determining the number of students in the class and finding a way to represent this number on paper. As students collect data about themselves, they think about the one-to-one correspondence between the number of people and the number of pieces of data. Developing strategies for keeping track of who has responded to a survey, recording data, and representing this information are important parts of Kindergarten work.

To begin to understand the processes involved in data analysis, kindergartners are involved in all phases of conducting a survey: They choose and pose a question, determine how to record responses, and count and make sense of the results.

Example: Do you like  ?

Yes	No
Carmen	Dennis
Mitchell	Timothy
Mary	Sarah
Tammy	Lisa
Raul	Kiyo
Jennifer	Latoya
	Lionel
	Manuel
	Yoshio
	Beth
	Russell

Students also use some of the data they collect to solve mathematical problems connected to their classroom. For example,

"25 students are in our class. 4 are absent. How many are here?"

Mathematical Emphases

Data Analysis

- Representing data

- Sorting and classifying

- Carrying out a data investigation

Benchmarks

- Represent a set of data.

- Use data to solve a problem.

- Sort a set of objects according to their attributes.

PART 4

Classroom Routines

Curriculum Unit	1	2	3	4	5	6	7
Classroom Routines							
Attendance	•	•	•	•	•	•	•
Calendar	•	•	•	•	•	•	•
Today's Question		•	•	•	•	•	•
Patterns on the Pocket Chart			•	•	•	•	•

Preview

Classroom Routines and Ten-Minute Math activities offer practice and review of key concepts at each grade level. The two types of activities differ mainly in how and when they are integrated into your class day. Classroom Routines appear throughout Grades K–2, and two are included in Grade 3. Ten-Minute Math activities appear in Grades 3–5.

Classroom Routines occur at regular intervals, perhaps during morning meeting, at the beginning of math class, or at another convenient time. These short activities, designed to take no longer than 10 minutes, support and balance the in-depth work of each curriculum unit. After their first introduction in a math session, they are intended for use outside of math time. Some teachers use them at the beginning or end of the day.

In Kindergarten, four Classroom Routines are woven through the seven curriculum units. The following pages contain complete procedures for these activities, including the variations intended for use in Kindergarten. Specific suggestions for use are found in Today's Plan for each session. It is recommended that you begin with suggested daily problems and adapt them to fit the needs of your students throughout the year. Any needed preparation is noted in the Investigation Planner.

Attendance

Students count their classmates to take attendance. Counting the class helps students develop strategies for counting accurately. Because classroom attendance data are important (i.e., submitted to the school office daily), *Attendance* offers a particularly good context for conversations about strategies for counting and keeping track, the importance of accuracy, and the need for double-checking a count.

Math Focus Points

Attendance provides regular practice with counting a quantity that is significant to students—the number of people in their class.

◆ Developing strategies for counting accurately

Materials and Preparation

• Make name tags by printing each student's name on a 4 × 6 index card. If possible, include a photo of the child. (These will also be used in *Today's Question*.)

Examples of students' nametags from one Kindergarten class

- *(Optional)* Make a sheet for recording each day's data and laminate it.

> ## Attendance
>
> We have _____ students in our class.
> _____ students are here today.
> _____ students are absent.

- Connecting cubes of one color (1 cube per student)—used to create an Attendance Stick

- Connecting cubes of one color (1 cube per student) and stick-on dots labeled with the numbers 1 through the total number of students in your class—used to create a numbered Attendance Stick

The basic activity is introduced gradually, over the course of Unit 1, *Who Is in School Today?*

Basic Activity

Step 1 **Establish who is absent.** Use the name tags to establish who is in the classroom and who is absent. (If each student finds and takes his or her name tag, the ones unclaimed represent students who are absent.)

Step 2 **Count the students in two ways.** Early in the year, point to each student as you count them aloud; then ask the class to count along with you. (See Session 1.1 in Unit 1, *Who Is in School Today?*) Counting around the Circle is introduced as one way to double-check the count. (See Session 1.2 in Unit 1, *Who Is in School Today?*)

As students become more comfortable with the counting sequence, they suggest and explore other ways to count and keep track; students also take on more responsibility for the actual counting and keeping track. For example, as one way of counting, a rotating attendance helper eventually counts the students in many primary classrooms. (The rotation could be on either a daily or weekly basis.)

Step 3 **Record the data.** After counting, record the total number of students in your class, the number present, and the number absent on your attendance recording sheet. (Alternatively, record it on the board or chart paper.)

Attendance

We have **25** students in our class.
23 students are here today.
2 students are absent.

Step 4 Use the Attendance Stick to represent the data.
Ask students to help you break the Attendance Stick so that it
represents the class today—one tower representing the number
of students present and one tower representing those who are
absent. (The class creates and first thinks about the Attendance
Stick in Session 1.6 in Unit 1, *Who Is in School Today?*)

*We counted and determined that Corey and Jason are
absent. Right now, our Attendance Stick has 25 cubes in
it. How can we make it show how many students are in
school* today? *What should I do to show that Corey and
Jason are absent?*

*Rebecca said to take 2 cubes off. There are 25 cubes in
our stick, and I took 2 cubes off, one for Corey and one
for Jason. How many cubes do you think are in the other
part of our Attendance Stick, the part that shows how
many students are here today?*

After gathering ideas, ask the students to count as you point
to each cube, to confirm the number. Discuss what the
towers show and how they relate to the data you counted and
recorded in steps 1 and 2.

**Step 5 Compare the towers to the numbered
Attendance Stick.** Use the numbered Attendance Stick to
think about how the number of students present (or absent)
compares to the number of students in the class. Place the
towers generated in step 3 next to the numbered Attendance
Stick and encourage students to describe what they notice.
(The class is introduced to the numbered Attendance Stick in
Session 2.5 in Unit 1, *Who Is in School Today?*)

We made a tower to show the number of students here
today and another tower to show how many are absent.
If I place those towers next to our numbered Attendance
Stick, what do you notice?

Variations

How Many Have Counted?

As usual, count around the circle to determine the total number of students present. In this variation, pause several times during the count to ask students how many people have counted.

Jack just said 7. How many people have counted so far? How do you know?

This variation helps students connect the counting numbers to the quantity they are counting—the number each student says stands for the number of people who have counted so far, and the last number represents the total number of students in class today. You can also use this variation to introduce and use terms like first, second, third, and so on, in a meaningful context:

So Jack said 7 because he was the seventh person in our circle. Who counted first? (Jae) What number did [Jae] say? (1)

What If We Start With . . . ?

Math Focus Point

◆ Considering whether order matters when you count

As usual, students count around the circle to determine the total number of students present. Then choose a different student and ask what will happen if the count starts with that student.

We started with Abby and counted around the circle. We found out that there are 24 students here today. What do you think would happen if we started with Carmen? Why do you think so?

Encourage students to explain their thinking. Then recount and discuss the results.

Comparing Groups

Math Focus Point

◆ Comparing quantities

This variation asks students to compare two groups, for example, the number present and absent or the number of girls and boys. After counting as usual, ask students if there are more students present or students absent and how they know. Once this is established, challenge students to determine how many more there are and to share their strategies. Have the Attendance Stick available for representing the situation and for modeling students' strategies. When comparing the number of girls and boys, students can line up to model the situation.

Counting Forward and Back

Math Focus Point

◆ Counting forward and backward

In this variation, students count around the circle to determine the total number of students in class today. Then they count backward from that total to 1. Beginning with the student who counted last means that each student will say the same number, but the count will be backward rather than forward. This variation helps students become familiar with the counting sequence in reverse, see counting back as another way to double-check a count, and begin to see the connection between counting forward and backward.

A Note About Counting Backward

Just like counting forward, students need to know the rote counting sequence and coordinate this with saying one number for each object. However, when counting backward, the first number said represents the total amount and each number subsequently said represents the removal of one object.

Calendar

Students count to establish the day and date. They use the calendar as a real-world tool for keeping track of time and events.

Math Focus Points

Calendar provides regular practice with the numbers and counting sequence to 31 plus a consistent review of the names and sequences of the days of the week.

◆ Using the calendar as a tool for keeping track of time

◆ Developing strategies for counting accurately

Materials and Preparation

Each month, prepare and post the current month on your pocket calendar, with all the dates showing. Make and place cards or tags for "Today" and for any special events that will happen (e.g., field trips, students' birthdays, visitors, school celebrations, holidays, days off), with a picture depicting the event (e.g., a cupcake with a candle or a sketch of the zoo).

An example of a pocket calendar for September

The basic activity is introduced over the course of Investigation 1 in Unit 1, *Who Is in School Today?*

Basic Activity

Step 1 Determine the day and date. Count up to today's date to establish the day and date. Help students connect those numbers to quantities by relating them to the number of days in the month so far: "1, 2, 3, 4, 5, ... So, there have been [5] days so far in September."

Look at the calendar to find the tag that shows Today. What is today's date? How can we figure out what number Today is?

Latoya counted 1, 2, 3, 4, 5, 6, 7 [*touching each number card*]. So today is the [seventh] day of [September]. The date is [September 7th].

As students become more comfortable with the calendar and the counting sequence, they take on more responsibility for the actual counting and keeping track. For example, a rotating calendar helper often leads this routine in many primary classrooms. Note that while many students can take on this role straightforwardly, some need an opportunity to preview what is expected of them before they lead the class in this routine. (The rotation could be on either a daily or weekly basis.)

Step 2 Occasionally, ask students about the tags that mark special days. (These tags are introduced in Session 1.3 in Unit 1, *Who Is in School Today?*)

Vary your questions, sometimes asking what day or date an event will (or did) happen, other times asking what will (or did) happen on a particular day or date. Still other times, focus on words and phrases, such as today, tomorrow, this week, next week, and last week. For example,

What day of the week will it be when we go to the zoo?

What will the date be when we go to the zoo?

Are we going to the zoo today? Tomorrow? Next week?

What is happening on Friday of this week?

What happened on the 12th day of October?

Keep in mind that there are different ways to refer to a date, for example, October 5, October 5th, and the 5th day of October. Vary the way you refer to dates so that students become comfortable with different forms. Saying "the 5th day of October" reinforces the idea that the calendar is a way to keep track of days in a month.

Teaching Note

Patterns on the Calendar

The Kindergarten calendar routine focuses on patterns inherent in the calendar and its structure: the counting sequence, 7 days in a week, the repeating cycle of 7 days (and 12 months), and so on. A classroom routine that focuses on repeating patterns is introduced in Unit 3, *What Comes Next?* See page 29 for more information about this routine.

Variations

A New Month

At the start of each month, change the monthly calendar to show the new month. Ask students what they notice about the new month. Some students focus on the arrangement of numbers or total number of days, while others note special events or pictures or designs on the calendar.

As the year progresses, encourage students to make comparisons between the months. Post the calendar for the new month next to the calendar for the month that is ending. Ask students to share their ideas about how the two calendars are similar and different.

Days of the Week

Use the calendar to review the days of the week, noting which days are school days and which are weekend (or nonschool) days.

How Many Days . . . ?

Ask students to figure out how long until (or since) a special event, such as a birthday, vacation, class trip, or holiday. For example,

How many more days until the storyteller comes to visit?

How many days has it been since our field trip to the aquarium?

Today is October 5. How many more days is it until October 15?

Students use the calendar to determine how many days and share their strategies for figuring this out.

What's Missing?

Choose a date or two (or cards for the days of the week) and remove them. Challenge the students to tell you which cards are missing and how they know.

Mixed-Up Calendar

Choose a date or two (or cards for the days of the week) and change their position on the calendar so that they are out of order. Challenge the students to find the mistakes and to help you fix them.

Today's Question

Students record their answer to a survey question with two possible answers on a two-column table. The class discussion focuses on describing and interpreting the data.

Math Focus Points

Today's Question provides students with regular opportunities to collect, record, and discuss data. It is also designed to provide regular practice with counting and comparing quantities.

◆ Collecting, counting, representing, describing, and comparing data

Today's Question is introduced in Sessions 3.1 and 3.5 in Unit 1, *Who Is in School Today?*

Materials

● Chart paper for making *Today's Question* charts according to specifications

● Markers

● Name tags (1 per student)

Basic Activity

Step 1 Prepare a chart for collecting the data, as suggested in the daily routine write-up. All recording sheets suggest some variation of a two-column table. For example,

Today's Question: Do You Have a Pet?	
Yes	No

Today's Question: Do You Have a Pet?	
Yes	No

Today's Question: Do You Have a Pet?	
Yes	
No	

Step 2 Explain the survey and collect the data. Read the question aloud and explain that students are to respond by writing their names in the appropriate column. They can use their name tags as a model for how to spell and write their names. Also, explain when students are to respond (e.g., as they arrive in the morning, during Math Workshop, during free time throughout the day).

Step 3 Discuss the data. Ask questions that encourage students to read the representation and to describe and interpret the data. For example,

What is this chart telling us?

What can you tell about [pets in our class] by looking at this chart?

How many people [have a pet]? How many people [don't have a pet]? Which group has *more*?

What else do you notice about the chart?

How many people responded to the survey? How do you know?

If we went to another classroom, collected the same kind of data, and made a chart, do you think that chart would look the same as or different from ours?

As this routine becomes familiar, students are asked to suggest different ways to organize the data as you collect it, to make it easier to see which group has more. Students' suggestions, such as writing names one over [under] the other, or drawing lines on the chart, are used to make subsequent *Today's Question* charts.

Today's Question: Do You Have a Pet?	
Yes	No

Patterns on the Pocket Chart

Students see part of a repeating pattern. They describe and extend the pattern, determining what would come next if the pattern were to continue. The focus is on repeating patterns made with two or three colors (shapes, etc.): AB [blue-green] patterns, ABC [blue-green-yellow] patterns, AAB [blue-blue-green] patterns, ABB [blue-green-green] patterns, and AABB [blue-blue-green-green] patterns.

Math Focus Points

When young students examine patterns, they look for relationships among the elements and explore how that information can be used to determine what comes next.

◆ Determining what comes next in a repeating pattern

◆ Describing repeating patterns

Materials

- Materials for making patterns (e.g., colored construction paper squares, square tiles, pattern blocks, arrow cards) that fit in the pockets on your chart

- Paper cup or baggie (1 per pair)

- A 10-by-10 pocket chart

- Resource Master M5, Question Mark Cards, from Unit 3, *What Comes Next?* (a set of 20–30)

Teaching Note

Pocket Charts

In this activity, students use the pocket 100 chart in the Kindergarten manipulatives kit. When you present longer patterns on this chart, you will have to help students understand that, when the row ends, the pattern continues on the second line. Some teachers use two pocket charts side by side, or a sentence pocket chart, so that students can look at and extend longer patterns without having the pattern "wrap around" to the next row.

Preparation

Prepare a small paper cup or plastic baggie per pair of students with at least one of each possible element of the pattern. For example, if you will investigate a pattern made from [colored square tiles], place one [square tile of each color] in each cup or bag. Because some students need to build the visible part of the pattern to figure out what might come next, prepare a few cups or baggies with *several* [tiles of each color].

Patterns on the Pocket Chart is introduced over the course of Investigation 2 in Unit 3, *What Comes Next?*

Basic Activity

Step 1 Secretly create a pattern in the first row of the chart. Arrange the repeating pattern specified in the daily routine write-up in the first row of the pocket chart. Cover the last four or five [square tiles] with Question Mark Cards.

An example of What Comes Next? *using square tiles in an AB repeating pattern*

Step 2 Card by card, reveal and discuss the pattern. Direct students' attention to the pocket chart. Discuss what students notice and then explain that you have built a pattern on the pocket chart, and that each time they see a Question Mark Card, they should think "What comes next?" and decide what [color] might be under that card.

If the pattern continues in the same way, what [color tile] do you think is under the first Question Mark Card? Talk to your partner and hold up the [tile] you think comes next.

Some students find it helpful to build the visible part of the pattern to determine what they think comes next.

Ask students to explain their choices. Then reveal the [tile] and follow the same process for each question mark. When the entire pattern is visible, say the name of each [color] aloud together, in order. Verbalizing the pattern they are considering often helps students internalize it, recognize any errors in the pattern, and determine what comes next. (See Session 2.2 in *What Comes Next?*)

Variations

Make Your Own Patterns

If the pocket 100 chart is hung where students can reach it, pairs can work together to make their own patterns during Math Workshop or free time. Pairs or small groups can also do *Patterns on the Pocket Chart,* with one student or pair creating a pattern and hiding some of it beneath Question Mark Cards and others determining what is beneath each question mark.

Wraparound Patterns

When students are familiar with the basic activity, they can investigate what happens to a pattern when it wraps around and continues to the next line. For example, if an AB pattern continues in a left-to-right progression, the pattern that emerges is the same one older students see when they investigate the patterns of odd and even numbers on the 100 chart.

An example of a Wraparound Pattern *using square tiles in an AB repeating pattern*

What Comes Here?

Determining what comes next is an important idea in learning about patterns. Also important is being able to look ahead and determine what comes here? even further down the line. Instead of asking for the next [color] in a pattern sequence, point to a pocket three or four squares along and ask students to say what [color] is under that question mark.

The teacher poses a What Comes Here? *question about an AB repeating pattern*

As you collect responses, ask students to explain how they determined the [color]. Some start at the beginning of the pattern, saying the [color] of each [tile] and then continuing that pattern as they touch the Question Mark Cards. Others use a similar strategy but start from the last visible [tile]:

The last [tile] showing is [pink]. [Green] comes after [pink], then [pink], then [green], then [pink].

A few may use what they know about the unit of the pattern (e.g., green-pink) and think about groups of two. These students might touch two cards at a time, knowing that the first in each pair is [green] and the second is [pink].

PART 5

Technology in *Investigations*

Preview

The *Investigations* curriculum incorporates two forms of technology: calculators and computers. In the early grades, students can begin to see how calculators can be used as mathematical tools. Computers are explicitly linked to one unit at each grade level through software that is provided with the curriculum.

Using Calculators with the Curriculum

During elementary school, students should become comfortable using a basic calculator as a tool that is common in their homes and communities. Increasingly sophisticated calculators are being developed and used in settings ranging from high school mathematics courses to science, business, and construction. Students need to learn how to use the calculator effectively and appropriately as a tool, just as they need to learn to read a clock, interpret a map, measure with a ruler, or use coins. They should use calculators for sensible purposes—just as you would do—not as a replacement for mental calculations or for pencil and paper calculations they are learning to do. While calculators are not explicitly used in Kindergarten, you can encourage students to use calculators to double-check calculations, as an aid if they have many calculations to carry out outside of math class, or to solve problems for which they can think out a solution but don't yet have the experience to carry out the computation.

For example, in one primary classroom, students became interested in the number of days in the year. Although these students were not yet able to add a string of 12 double-digit numbers, they could articulate a sound strategy—adding the number of days in each month—and use a calculator to carry it out.

Look for situations in the classroom such as this one, where the purpose of the mathematical activity is not developing computational fluency and when the numbers and calculations are beyond the students' skills in written or mental computation. These situations provide opportunities for students to practice estimating reasonable results, then carrying out the calculation with a calculator.

Students enjoy using what they perceive as an adult tool. Investigating with the calculator gives students an opportunity to notice mathematical patterns and to ask questions about mathematical symbols. For example, in a second-grade class, students were dividing lots of numbers by 2, which led to a discussion of the meaning of 0.5. In a fourth-grade class, some students became intrigued with the square root sign. The teacher challenged them to systematically keep track of the results of applying the square root symbol to whole numbers, starting with 1, and to come up with an idea about its meaning.

The calculator is an efficient tool for many purposes in life, and students should learn to use it sensibly, knowing that using it well depends on the user's correct analysis and organization of the problem, comparing its results with reasonable estimates, and double-checking.

Introducing and Managing the *Shapes* Software in Kindergarten

Shapes Software is provided as a component of the *Investigations* curriculum. The *Software Support Reference Guide* provides a complete description of the software and instructions for using the software activities.

The *Shapes* Software is formally introduced in Kindergarten, Unit 5, *Make a Shape, Build a Block.* The software activities are integrated into Math Workshop and both extend and deepen the mathematical ideas emphasized in this unit. In some cases the software activities allow students to work with geometric shapes in ways that they are not able to in the noncomputer activities. Therefore, while using this software is optional, we recommend its use if you have computers either in your classroom or in your school's computer lab.

Read the **Teacher Notes:** Introducing and Managing the *Shapes* Software (Unit 5, p. 138) and About the Math in the *Shapes* Software (Unit 5, p. 141) for further information about the software, about introducing and integrating computer work into your classroom, about the mathematics content of the activities, and about managing the computer environment.

Options for Introducing the *Shapes* Software

How you introduce and incorporate these computer activities into your curriculum depends on the number of computers and computer technology that you have available.

- *Computer lab:* If you have a computer laboratory with one computer for each pair of students, the entire class can become familiar with the computer activities at the same time. In this case, you will not need to devote time during math class to introduce the new software activity. Once an activity has been introduced, students can do it either during Math Workshop (if you have classroom computers) or during their scheduled lab time.

- *Large projection screen:* If you have a large projection screen, you can introduce the software activities to the whole class during a math session, immediately before Math Workshop or at another time of the day.

- *Small groups of students:* With fewer classroom computers, you can introduce the activities to small groups either before or during Math Workshop. These students can then be paired and become peer "teachers" of the software.

Regardless of the number of computers available, students generally benefit from working on these activities in pairs. This not only maximizes computer resources but also encourages students to consult, monitor, and teach one another. Generally, more than two students at one computer find it difficult to share. You may need to monitor computer use more closely than the other Math Workshop choices to ensure that all students get sufficient computer time. Each pair should spend at least 15–20 minutes at the computer for each activity.

Managing the Computer Environment

Students should be using the *Shapes* Software consistently throughout Unit 5 and periodically for the rest of the school year. If you have daily access to a computer lab, you might take advantage of this to supplement your regular math class. If your school has a computer teacher, you might collaborate with that teacher to have students work on *Shapes* activities during some of their scheduled lab time.

More typically, a classroom will have a small number of computers. With computers in the classroom, pairs of students can cycle through the software activities during Math Workshop, just as they cycle through the other choices. Three to five classroom computers is ideal, but even with only one or two, students can have a successful computer experience. When you have fewer computers, find additional computer time for students throughout the day, outside of math.

Using *Shapes* All Year

Unit 5 is the only unit in the Kindergarten sequence that explicitly uses the *Shapes* software. However, we recommend that students continue using it for the remainder of the school year. With more experience, they become more fluent in the mechanics of the software itself and can better focus on the designs they want to make and how to select and arrange shapes for those designs. They can work with the tangram shapes as well as the pattern block and power polygon shapes, can solve the many different kinds of puzzles that come with the software, and make their own puzzles.

PART 6

Professional Development

Teacher Notes in *Investigations*

Teacher Notes are one of the most important professional development tools in *Investigations*. Each curriculum unit contains a collection of Teacher Notes that offer information about the mathematical content of that unit and how students learn it.

In this section of *Implementing Investigations in Kindergarten,* you will find a set of Teacher Notes that addresses topics and issues applicable to the curriculum as a whole rather than to specific curriculum units.

These Teacher Notes provide important background about approaches to mathematics teaching and learning, about critical features of the mathematics classroom, and about how to develop an inclusive mathematics community in which all students participate. You can benefit from reading these notes, either individually or as the basis for discussion in teacher study groups, before starting to use the curriculum. Alternatively, you can read these notes gradually throughout the year while you are using the curriculum in your classroom. These brief essays take on new resonance and meaning as you have more experience with student learning and the *Investigations* curriculum. Plan to return to this collection periodically to review the ideas and reflect on the implications for classroom practice.

A complete list of the Teacher Note titles from each of the nine curriculum units is included on pages 61–62.

Teacher Note

Computational Fluency and Place Value

Computational fluency includes accuracy, flexibility, and efficiency. When fluency with a particular operation is achieved, students can look at the problem as a whole, choose a solution strategy that they can carry out easily without becoming bogged down or losing track of their steps, use their strategy to solve the problem accurately, recognize whether the result is reasonable, and double-check their work. Students who are fluent have a repertoire that includes mental strategies, strategies in which only intermediate steps are jotted down while other steps are carried out mentally, and strategies that require a complete written solution. They are flexible in their choice of algorithm or procedure, and they can use one method to check another.

Developing computational fluency with whole numbers is central to the elementary curriculum. This development includes the building blocks of computation:

- Understanding the base-ten number system and its place value notation

- Understanding the meaning of the operations and their relationships

- Knowing the basic addition and multiplication number combinations (the "facts") and their counterparts for subtraction and division

- Estimating reasonable results

- Interpreting problems embedded in contexts and applying the operations correctly to these problems

- Learning, practicing, and consolidating accurate and efficient strategies for computing

- Developing curiosity about numbers and operations, their characteristics, and how they work

- Learning to articulate, represent, and justify generalizations

At each grade level, computational fluency looks different. Students are progressing in learning the meaning of the four arithmetic operations with whole numbers, developing methods grounded in this meaning, and gradually solving problems of greater difficulty through the grades. At each grade level, benchmarks for whole number computation indicate what is expected of all students by the end of each curriculum unit and each grade, although work at each grade level goes beyond these benchmarks. Gradually, approaches to problems become more efficient, flexible, and accurate. For example, in Grade 1, many students begin the year adding by direct modeling of the problem with objects and counting the sum by ones. By the end of the year, students are expected to start with one of the quantities and count on the other, and for some combinations students "just know" the sum or use known combinations to solve others ("I know $4 + 4 = 8$, so $4 + 5 = 9$"). In Grade 4, many students start the year solving some multiplication problems by skip counting, but by the end of the year, they are expected to solve multidigit multiplication problems such as 34×68 by breaking problems into subproblems, based on the distributive property.

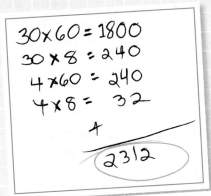

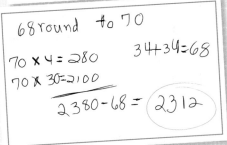

Sample Student Work

Understanding the Base-Ten Number System

Learning about whole number computation is closely connected to learning about the base-ten number system. The base-ten number system is a "place value" system. That is, any numeral, say 2, can represent different values, depending on where it appears in a written number: it can represent 2 ones, 2 tens, 2 hundreds, 2 thousands, as well as 2 tenths, 2 hundredths, and so forth. Understanding this place value system requires coordinating the way we write the numerals that represent a particular number (e.g., 217) and the way we name numbers in words (e.g., two hundred seventeen) with how those symbols represent quantities.

The heart of this work is relating written numerals to the quantity and to how the quantity is composed. It builds from work on tens and ones in Grades 1 and 2 to a focus on numbers in the hundreds and thousands in Grade 3, and work with numbers in the ten thousands, hundred thousands, and beyond in Grades 4 and 5. Knowing place value is not simply a matter of saying that 217 "has 2 hundreds, 1 ten, and 7 ones," which students can easily learn to do by following a pattern without attaching much meaning to what they are saying. Students must learn to visualize how 217 is built up from hundreds, tens, and ones, in a way that helps them relate its value to other quantities. Understanding the place value of a number such as 217 entails knowing, for example, that 217 is closer to 200 than to 300, that it is 100 more than 117, that it is 17 more than 200, that it is 3 less than 220, and that it is composed of 21 tens and 7 ones.

A thorough understanding of the base-ten number system is one of the critical building blocks for developing computational fluency. Understanding place value is at the heart of estimating and computing. For example, consider adding two different quantities to 32:

$32 + 30 = \underline{\hspace{2cm}}$

$32 + 3 = \underline{\hspace{2cm}}$

How much will 32 increase in each case? Students think about how the first sum will now have 6 tens, but the ones will not change, whereas in the second sum, the ones will change, but the tens remain the same. Adding three *tens* almost doubles 32, while adding three *ones* increases its value by a small amount. Considering the place value of numbers that are being added, subtracted, multiplied, or divided provides the basis for developing a reasonable estimate of the result.

The composition of numbers from multiples of 1, 10, 100, 1,000, and so forth, is the basis for most of the strategies students adopt for whole number operations. Students' computational algorithms and procedures depend on knowing how to decompose numbers and knowing the effects of operating with multiples of 10. For example, one of the most common algorithms for addition is adding by place. Each number is decomposed into ones, tens, hundreds, and so forth; these parts are then combined. For example,

$326 + 493$

$300 + 400 = 700$

$20 + 90 = 110$

$6 + 3 = 9$

$700 + 110 + 9 = 819$

To carry out this algorithm fluently, students must know a great deal about place value, not just how to decompose numbers. They must also be able to apply their knowledge of single-digit sums such as $3 + 4$ and $2 + 9$ to sums such as $300 + 400$ and $20 + 90$. In other words, they know how to interpret the place value of numbers *as they operate with them*—in this case, that just as 2 ones plus 9 ones equals 11 ones, 2 tens plus 9 tens equals 11 tens, or 110.

As with addition, algorithms for multidigit multiplication also depend on knowing how the place value of numbers is interpreted as numbers are multiplied. Again, students must understand how they can apply knowledge of single-digit combinations such as 3×4 to solve problems such as 36×42.

For example,

36×42

$30 \times 40 = 1{,}200$

$30 \times 2 = 60$

$6 \times 40 = 240$

$6 \times 2 = 12$

$1{,}200 + 240 + 60 + 12 = 1{,}512$

Students gradually learn how a knowledge of 3×4 helps them solve 30×4, 3×40, 30×40, 3×400, and so forth.

Building Computational Fluency Over Time

There is a tremendous amount of work to do in the area of numbers and operations in Grades K–5.

- Kindergartners and first graders are still working on coordinating written and spoken numbers with their quantitative meaning.

- Second graders are uncovering the relationship between 10 ones and 1 ten and between 10 tens and 1 hundred.

- Third graders are immersed in how the properties of multiplication differ from the properties of addition.

- Fourth and fifth graders are solving multidigit problems and becoming flexible in their use of a number of algorithms.

This list provides only a brief glimpse of how much work there is to do in these grades.

Students gain computational fluency in each operation through several years of careful development. Extended time across several grades is spent on each operation. Students build computational fluency with small numbers as they learn about the meaning and properties of the operation. Then they gradually expand their work to more difficult

problems as they develop, analyze, compare, and practice general methods.

Let's use subtraction as an example of this process:

- In Kindergarten and Grade 1, students solve subtraction problems by modeling the action of subtraction.

- By Grade 2, students are articulating and using the inverse relationship between addition and subtraction to solve problems like the following: "If I have 10 cookies, how many more cookies do I need to bake so I have 24?"

- During Grades 2 and 3, students become fluent with the subtraction "facts" and model and solve a variety of types of subtraction problems, including comparison and missing part problems. By Grade 3, as students' understanding of the base-ten number system grows, they use their understanding of place value to solve problems with larger numbers.

- In Grades 3 and 4, students articulate, represent, and justify important generalizations about subtraction. For example, if you add the same amount to (or subtract it from) each number in a subtraction expression, the difference does not change, as in the equation $483 - 197 = 486 - 200$. In these grades, students also choose one or two procedures, practice them, and expand their command of these procedures with multidigit numbers.

- In Grades 4 and 5, as their fluency with subtraction increases, students analyze and compare strategies for solving subtraction problems. Because they are fluent with more "transparent" algorithms for subtraction in which the place value of the numbers is clear, they are now in a position to appreciate the shortcut notation of the U.S. traditional regrouping algorithm for subtraction, analyze how it works, and compare it to other algorithms. (See the Teacher Note, Computational Algorithms and Methods.)

This account gives only a glimpse of the work involved in understanding subtraction across the grades. Each operation has a similar complexity. It is critical that the time and depth required for the careful development of ideas is devoted to this strand. For this reason, in each of Grades 1–4, there are four units spread throughout the year that focus on whole numbers, operations, and the base-ten number system. In Kindergarten, three units focus on counting, quantity, and modeling addition and subtraction. In Grade 5, because of the increased emphasis on rational numbers, three units focus on whole numbers and two units focus on fractions, decimals, and percents. The whole number units within each grade build on each other in a careful sequence.

As you work with your students on whole number computation, here are some questions to keep in mind as you assess their progress toward computational fluency [adapted from Russell, 2000, p. 158]:

- Do students know and draw on basic facts and other number relationships?

- Do students use and understand the structure of the base-ten number system? For example, do students know the result of adding 100 to 2,340 or multiplying 40 × 500?

- Do students recognize related problems that can help with the problem?

- Do students use relationships among operations?

- Do students know what each number and numeral in the problem means (including subproblems)?

- Can students explain why the steps being used actually work?

- Do students have a clear way to record and keep track of their procedures?

- Do students have more than one approach for solving problems in each operation? Can they determine which problems lend themselves to different methods?

Supporting Computational Fluency Across the Curriculum

Work in the other content areas also connects to and supports the work on computational fluency in the number and operations units. For example, an emphasis on the foundations of algebra across the grades opens up important opportunities to strengthen work with numbers and operations. Within the number and operations units themselves, articulation, representation, and justification of general claims about the operations (an aspect of early algebraic thinking) strengthen students' understanding of the operations (see the Teacher Note, Foundations of Algebra in the Elementary Grades, and the Algebra Connections essay in each of the number and operations units). The work with functions provides interesting problem contexts in which students' work on ratio and on constant rates of change connect to and support their work on multiplication (see the Teacher Note, Foundations of Algebra in the Elementary Grades, and the Algebra Connections essay in each of the patterns, functions, and change units). Geometry and measurement units also provide contexts in which students revisit multiplication. Finally, the Classroom Routines (in Grades K–3) and Ten-Minute Math (in Grades 3–5) provide ongoing, regular practice of estimation and computation.

Reference

Russell, S. J. (2000). Developing computational fluency with whole numbers. *Teaching Children Mathematics 7*, 154–158.

Teacher Note

Computational Algorithms and Methods

In the elementary grades, a central part of students' work is learning about addition, subtraction, multiplication, and division and becoming fluent and flexible in solving whole number computation problems. In the *Investigations* curriculum, students use methods and algorithms in which they can see clearly the steps of their solution and focus on the mathematical sense of what they are doing. They use and compare several different methods to deepen their understanding of the properties of the operations and to develop flexibility in solving problems. They practice methods for each operation so that they can use them efficiently to solve problems.

What Is an Algorithm?

An algorithm is a series of well-defined steps used to solve a certain class of problem (for example, all addition problems). Often, the sequence of steps is repeated with successive parts of the problem. For example, here is an example of an addition algorithm:

$$249 + 674$$

$$200 + 600 = 800$$

$$40 + 70 = 110$$

$$9 + 4 = 13$$

$$800 + 110 + 13 = 923$$

Written instructions for this algorithm might begin as follows:

1. Find the left-most place represented in the addends and add all the amounts in that place.

2. Move one place to the right and add all the amounts in that place in all the addends.

3. Repeat step 2 until all parts of all addends have been added.

4. Add the sums of each place.

To specify these instructions, as if we were going to teach them to a computer, we would have more work to do to make them even more specific and precise. For example, how is step 4 carried out? Should each place be added separately again and then combined? In practice, when students and adults use this algorithm, the partial sums that must be added in step 4 are generally easy enough to add mentally, as they are in this problem, although occasionally one might again break up some of the numbers.

Algorithms like this one, once understood and practiced, are general methods that can be used for a whole class of problems. The adding by place algorithm, for example, can be generalized for use with any addition problem. As students' knowledge of the number system expands, they learn to apply this algorithm to, for example, larger numbers or to decimals. Students also learn how to use clear and concise notation, to carry out some steps mentally, and to record those intermediate steps needed so that they can keep track of the solution process.

Nonalgorithmic Methods for Computing with Whole Numbers

Students also learn methods for computing with whole numbers that are not algorithmic—that is, one cannot completely specify the steps for carrying them out, and they do not generally involve a repetition of steps. However, these methods are studied because they are useful for solving certain problems. In thinking through why and how they work, students also deepen their understanding of the properties of the various operations. This work provides opportunities for students to articulate generalizations about the operations and to represent and justify them.

For example, here is one method a third grader might use to solve this problem:

$$\$7.46 + \$3.28 = \$7.50 + \$3.24 = \$10.74$$

The student changed the addition expression to an equivalent expression with numbers that made it easier to find the sum mentally. First graders often use this idea as they learn some of their addition combinations, transforming a combination they are learning into an equivalent combination they already know: $7 + 5 = 6 + 6 = 12$.

When students try to use the same method to make a subtraction problem easier to solve, they find that they must modify their method to create an equivalent problem. Instead of adding an amount to one number and subtracting it from the other, as in addition, they must add the same amount to (or subtract it from) each number:

$$182 - 69 = 183 - 70 = 113$$

Throughout the *Investigations* curriculum, methods like these are introduced and studied to deepen students' understanding of how these operations work and to engage them in proving their ideas using representations of the operations.

Because the ways in which a problem might be changed to make an equivalent problem that is easier to solve can vary (although it might be possible to precisely specify a particular variant of one of these methods), these methods are not algorithms. Students do not generally use such methods to solve a whole class of problems (e.g., any addition problem); rather, students who are flexible in their understanding of numbers and operations use finding equivalent expressions as one possible method and notice when a problem lends itself to solving in this way.

Learning Algorithms Across the Grades

In *Investigations,* students develop, use, and compare algorithms and other methods. These are not "invented" but are constructed with teacher support, as students' understanding of the operations and the base-ten number system grow (see the Teacher Note, Computational Fluency and Place Value). Because the algorithms that students learn are so grounded in knowledge of the operation and the number system, most of them arise naturally as students progress from single-digit to multidigit problems. For example, the adding by place addition algorithm shown earlier naturally grows out of what students are learning about how a number such as 24 is composed of 2 tens and 4 ones. It is part of the teacher's role to make these methods explicit, help students understand and practice them, and support students to gradually use more efficient methods. For example, a second grader who is adding on one number in parts might solve $49 + 34$ by adding on 10, then another 10, then another 10, then 4 to 49 ($49 + 10 + 10 + 10 + 4$). By having this student compare solutions with another student's whose first step is $49 + 30$, the teacher helps the first student analyze what is the same and different about their solutions and opens up the possibility for the first student of a more efficient method—adding on a multiple of 10 all at once rather than breaking it into 10s.

The algorithms and other methods that students learn about and use in *Investigations* for multidigit problems are characterized by their *transparency*. Transparent algorithms

- make the properties of the operations visible.

- show the place value of the numbers in the problem.

- make clear how a problem is broken into subproblems and how the results of these subproblems are recombined.

These characteristics are critical for students while they are learning the meaning of the operations and are building their understanding of the base-ten system. Here is an example of a transparent multiplication algorithm that might be used by a fourth grader:

$$
\begin{array}{r}
34 \\
\times\ 78 \\
\hline
2100 \\
280 \\
240 \\
32 \\
\hline
\end{array}
$$

$$2{,}000 + 500 + 150 + 2 = 2{,}652$$

In this algorithm, students record all numbers fully, showing the place value of all the digits. Because the result of each multiplication is shown, the application of the distributive property is kept track of clearly.

There is a misperception that many different algorithms might arise in a single classroom and that this multitude of algorithms will be confusing. In fact, there are only a few basic algorithms and methods for each operation that arise from students' work and that are emphasized in the curriculum. Each is tied closely to how students solve problems and to the basic characteristics and properties of the operation. Teacher Notes throughout the curriculum provide more detail about these methods.

Students can and do develop efficiency and fluency with these more transparent algorithms. As they do, they do some steps mentally and may no longer need to write out every step to keep track of their work. For example, in using the adding by place algorithm to add $249 + 674$, a competent user might simply jot down 800, 110, 13, and then add those partial sums mentally and record the answer. There may be times when you require students to write out their complete solution method so that you can see how they are solving problems, but for everyday use, efficient users of such algorithms will record only the steps they need.

These algorithms and methods are studied, compared, and analyzed for different reasons. All of them are transparent, preserve place value, and make visible important properties such as distributivity. Some can be practiced and provide general, efficient methods. Others are useful only for particular problems but are studied because of what they illuminate about the operations.

Studying the U.S. Standard Algorithms

The U.S. standard algorithms for addition, subtraction, and multiplication are also explicitly studied in *Investigations* but only after students are fully grounded in understanding the operation and using transparent algorithms for multidigit computation. These algorithms were developed for efficiency and compactness for handwritten computation. When these algorithms are used as a primary teaching tool, their very compactness, which can be an advantage for experienced users, becomes a disadvantage for young learners because they obscure the place value of the numbers and the properties of the operation.

Some students do use the standard algorithms with understanding. As these algorithms come up in class, they should be incorporated into the list of class strategies. Teachers should make sure that students who use them understand what the shortcut notation represents and that they can explain why these algorithms make sense. They should also know and understand other methods. In Grade 4, students revisit the U.S. standard addition algorithm formally, analyze how and why it works, and compare it to other algorithms they are using. In Grade 5, students revisit the U.S. standard subtraction and multiplication algorithms in the same way. Division methods studied in this curriculum focus on the inverse relationship between multiplication and division.

Teacher Note

Representations and Contexts for Mathematical Work

Mathematics involves describing and analyzing all kinds of mathematical relationships. Throughout the *Investigations* curriculum, students use representations and contexts to help them visualize these mathematical relationships. Thinking with representations and contexts allows students to express and further develop their ideas and enables students to engage with each other's ideas. Whether solving a multiplication problem, finding the area of a rectangle, describing the relationship between two variables, or ordering fractions, students use representations and contexts to investigate and explain.

The *Investigations* curriculum introduces a limited number of carefully chosen representations and contexts because they provide representations of mathematical relationships that students can use to solve problems and/or to show their ideas and solutions to others. Students may first use representations or contexts concretely, drawing or modeling with materials. Later, they incorporate these representations and contexts into mental models that they can call on to visualize the structure of problems and their solutions. Students develop the habit of making drawings, building models, and using representations to think with and to explain their thinking to others. They develop a repertoire of representations that they know well and can apply when faced with unfamiliar problem situations.

Good contexts and representations have the following characteristics:

- They are useful for a whole class of problems (e.g., addition problems).

- They can be extended to accommodate more complex problems and/or students' expanding repertoire of numbers.

- They do not overwhelm or interfere with the focus on mathematical content.

- Their structure embodies important characteristics of the mathematical relationships.

This Teacher Note provides some examples of how models, materials, and contexts are used by students across the grades.

Representations

Basic representations in the *Investigations* curriculum include connecting cubes, the 100 chart (and its variants, the 300, 1,000, and 10,000 charts), number lines, arrays, and sets of two-dimensional (2-D) and three-dimensional (3-D) shapes. Each representation provides access to certain characteristics, actions, and properties of numbers and operations or of geometric properties and relationships. Here are two examples.

Connecting Cubes

Connecting cubes are a basic material for counting and for modeling addition and subtraction in Grades K–2. The cubes are a discrete model of whole numbers and provide a uniform counting material for representing ones. Because they connect, they can be organized into sticks of ten cubes so that students can use them to represent tens and ones.

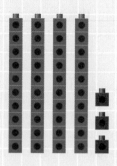

The individual cubes are visible in the connected stick of ten, so students can visualize how this stick represents the equivalence of 1 ten and 10 ones and then how 10 ten-sticks is equivalent to 1 hundred and 100 ones. Connecting cubes are a flexible material. They are well suited for modeling the basic actions of joining and separating. They can also be used to construct rectangular arrays for studying multiplication and area. Students also use the cubes to construct rectangular prisms and to analyze and visualize how the volume of the shape consists of a certain number of layers, each of which has the same dimensions.

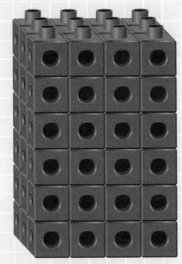

Each layer is 3 × 4. There are six layers.

The Number Line

The number line is another key representation of numbers. This continuous representation offers students another view of the number sequence and number relationships. Students' beginning work with number lines involves number lines that are already marked with the counting numbers.

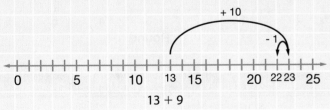

13 + 9

I jumped up 10 to 23, then back 1.

Later, students choose the part of the number line they need and which points on it should be marked as they use it to solve problems.

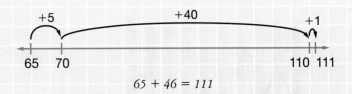

65 + 46 = 111

The number line provides access to the idea that numbers are infinite. At first, students come to this idea in relation to the counting sequence of whole numbers. Later, as they encounter negative numbers, they consider how the number line extends in both directions, that both positive and negative numbers "go on forever." In their study of rational numbers, they use the number line to model fractions and decimal fractions and consider how the segments of the number line between two successive whole numbers can be divided into smaller and smaller pieces. In later years, they will come to understand that there are an infinite number of numbers between any two successive integers.

For students to use a representation well, they need enough experience with it so that they understand its basic characteristics and can then use it themselves to model and solve problems. For example, using an unmarked number line flexibly requires that students have enough prior experience using the marked number line to count, add, and subtract.

Using Different Representations

Different representations offer different models of the mathematics and access to different mathematical ideas. For example, both place value models and number lines are useful in students' study of subtraction, but they each allow students to see different aspects of subtraction. A student solving the problem 103 − 37 might think about subtracting 37 in parts by visualizing a place value model of the numbers, subtracting 3 tens and then 7 ones (which, for ease of subtraction from 103, the student might split into 3 + 4).

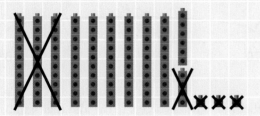

Another student might think about creating an easier, equivalent problem: $103 - 37 = 106 - 40$. This student might visualize "sliding" the interval from 37 to 103 along a number line to determine how to change the numbers, while preserving the difference between them.

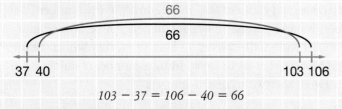

$$103 - 37 = 106 - 40 = 66$$

More details about these and other representations are provided throughout the curriculum units.

Contexts

Contexts and stories are also used to represent mathematical relationships. A good context can be created from familiar events or fantasy. Contexts that students can imagine and visualize give them access to ways of thinking about the mathematical ideas and relationships they are studying. For a context to be useful, it must be connected enough to students' experience that students can imagine and represent the actions and relationships. At the same time, the details of the context need not be elaborate, so that the nonmathematical aspects of the context stay in the background. Here are two examples.

The Penny Jar

One of the contexts in the patterns and functions units in Grades 1 and 4 is the Penny Jar. The Penny Jar contains some number of pennies (the starting amount) and then has a certain number of pennies added to it each day or with each round (the constant rate of change). This is one of the contexts used to engage students in exploring a function—the relationship of the number of days to the total number of pennies—that involves a constant rate of change. Students' knowledge of similar real-world contexts engages students quickly in the mathematics and helps them visualize the mathematical relationships, but it is not so elaborate that it obscures or distracts from the mathematics.

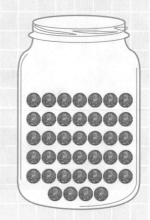

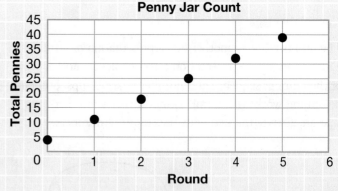

Number of Rounds	Total Number of Pennies
Start	4
1	11
2	18
3	25
4	32
5	39

Once students are familiar with the Penny Jar context, they can represent it in multiple ways, using pictures, tables, and graphs, to describe and analyze the relationship between the two variables.

Travel Stories

In Grade 3, travel stories are used as a context for subtraction. Students are familiar with taking trips by car or bus or have encountered such trips in stories or movies. They know about a trip having a starting point, an ending point, and a certain distance traveled. They are also familiar with stopping along the way for a meal or to take a break and with discussing how much of the distance has been covered and how much is still ahead of them.

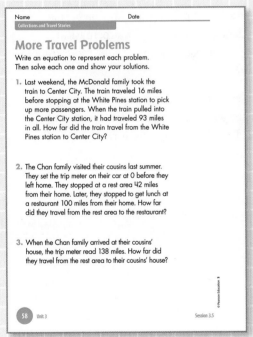

▲ Grade 3 Unit 3 *Student Activity Book*, page 58

Helping Students Connect to Contexts

Teachers often personalize these contexts for students to help them visualize and use it. For example, when using the Penny Jar context, one first-grade teacher had a brief discussion about places they or someone else they know used to hold money and some reasons that money might get added to any of these. The teacher then referred to some of these situations as they discussed problems, "Let's say we're talking about Andre's situation when he is doing his chores. He has 3 pennies in the jar, and he is going to put in 2 pennies for each chore he completes." In using the travel story context, teachers also refer to situations that are familiar to students: "So let's say Janelle and her family are setting off to visit her grandma, like they did last summer, and the whole trip is 274 miles. …"

More details about these and other contexts are provided throughout the curriculum units.

Using Representations and Contexts

Representations and contexts are central in mathematics at all levels for investigating, explaining, and justifying mathematical ideas. Students should move toward developing mental models of mathematical relationships that they call on routinely and will often use pictures, diagrams, and objects when they encounter new kinds of problems.

Students should use representations and contexts judiciously and with purpose. A first grader who is solving word problems that involve addition and subtraction might model every problem with cubes. Another student in the same class might model one or two problems; then, having visually confirmed the action of the operation, the student might solve the rest by imagining one quantity and counting on. A third student—or the same student later in the year—might reason about the numbers without using an image or model. In class discussions, both the teacher and students use representations to clarify and investigate mathematical ideas and to help all students focus on what is being discussed.

As a teacher, one of your roles is to support students in using representations and contexts and to help them develop mental images that they can call on. On the one hand, students need not show a picture for a problem when they have developed more efficient numerical tools and methods. For example, when one fourth grader was asked to solve a multiplication problem in two ways, he solved the problem by breaking it up efficiently, using the distributive property, and then showed a solution using groups of tally marks. His teacher let him know that using tally marks was not what she was looking for from him and reminded him of the work the class had been doing on changing one of the numbers in the problem and then adjusting the product.

On the other hand, students should understand that the use of representations and models is not a "crutch" in mathematics but are a powerful set of tools for investigating problem situations. In the classroom, encourage representation as a central part of mathematics activity. Make a habit of asking questions such as these:

- Is there a way you can show us your thinking using the number line or the 100 chart?

- Can you explain how your strategy makes sense using the travel context we have been using for some of the problems?

- You used a number line and Chris used a place-value sketch showing tens and ones. What is similar or different about these two approaches? Where can you see the four tens in Chris's place value sketch on Luc's number line solution?

- Karen, you are thinking of the multiplication problem as representing 47 classrooms with 23 students in each class. How did this context help you keep track of the parts of the problem?

- Can you show us with a picture or on the Geoboard what you mean when you say "a triangle is half of a rectangle"?

- What if you needed to explain or prove what you are saying to someone who came to visit our classroom? Is there a way you can show me why what you are saying is true with a picture or diagram?

When students are accustomed to incorporating representations in their daily mathematics work and considering what representations can be helpful for explaining mathematical ideas, they can also create their own images appropriate to a particular problem situation. Help students make these images simple enough so that they serve the mathematics rather than obscure it. The use of representations in class discussions helps illuminate students' ideas for each other and, by putting out an image that is available to all students, clarifies what mathematical relationships are being considered and invites more students into the conversation.

For further examples of students' use of representations, see the classroom stories in the section "Language and Representation" in Part 7, Working with the Range of Learners: Classroom Cases.

Teacher Note

Foundations of Algebra in the Elementary Grades

Algebra is a multifaceted area of mathematics content that has been described and classified in different ways. Across many of the classification schemes, four areas foundational to the study of algebra stand out: (1) generalizing and formalizing patterns; (2) representing and analyzing the structure of numbers and operations; (3) using symbolic notation to express functions and relations; and (4) representing and analyzing change.

In the *Investigations* curriculum, these areas of early algebra are addressed in two major ways: (1) work within the counting, number, and operations units focusing on generalizations that arise in the course of students' study of numbers and operations and (2) a coherent strand, consisting of one unit in each grade, K–5, that focuses on patterns, functions, and change. These two areas of emphasis are described here, followed by some additional information about the goals of work on early algebra in the curriculum.

Early Algebra: Making General Claims About Numbers and Operations

Each *Investigations* unit on counting, numbers, and operations includes a focus on reasoning and generalizing about numbers and operations. Even in beginning work with numbers and operations in Kindergarten and Grade 1, students are already noticing regularities about numbers and operations. For example, in the K–1 game *Double Compare,* each student in the pair selects two number cards. The student with the greater sum says "me." In this early work, before students know their single-digit addition combinations, most students are counting all or counting on to determine the sum. But consider how students are reasoning in the following brief episode:

> Bridget and Siva are playing *Double Compare.* Bridget draws a 5 and a 2; Siva draws a 5 and a 3 and immediately says "me," indicating that he has the greater sum. Siva usually counts both amounts by ones to get the sum, so the teacher asks him, "How did you know you have more?" Siva responds, "Because I have a 3 and she has a 2, and 3 is bigger." Bridget is nodding vigorously and adds, "The 5s don't count."

How are the students in this episode figuring out who has the greater sum? Why does Siva only compare 3 with 2, and what does Bridget mean when she says the "5s don't count"? Implicit in these students' work is a general claim about adding numbers that many young students use: If you are comparing two addition expressions, and one of the addends in the first expression is the same as one of the addends in the second, then you need only compare the other two addends to determine which expression has the greater sum. This is a mouthful to put into words, and students might not be able to articulate this idea completely; nevertheless, they are reasoning based on this idea. In later years, this idea can be represented with symbolic notation:

For any numbers a, b, c, and d when $a = c$ and $b < d$, then $a + b < c + d$.

$a = c$	$b < d$	$a + b < c + d$
$5 = 5$	$2 < 3$	$5 + 2 < 5 + 3$

Part of the teaching work in the elementary grades is to help students articulate, represent, investigate, and justify such general claims that arise naturally in the course of their work with numbers and operations. In each of the number and operations units in Grades K–5, the Algebra Connections essay highlights several of these general ideas about properties and relationships relevant to the work in that curriculum unit, with examples of how students think about and represent them. Investigation and discussion of some of these generalizations are built into unit sessions; for others, Algebra Notes alert the teacher to activities or discussions in which these ideas are likely to arise and could be pursued.

In the course of articulating, representing, and justifying their ideas about such general claims, students in the elementary grades are beginning to engage in proving—a central part of mathematics. They consider the questions: Does this generalization apply to *all* numbers (in the domain under consideration, usually whole numbers)? Why does it work? How do you know? In two of the number and operations units in each grade, 2–5, you will find a Teacher Note that focuses on proof and justification. These Teacher Notes provide examples of the ways that students at that grade level engage in proving and how their proofs, based on representations, are related to the proofs a mathematician might carry out.

Examples of the general claims highlighted in the curriculum in Grades K–2 are as follows:

- Counting the same set of objects in different orders results in the same count.

- If one number is larger than another, and the same number is added to each, the first total will be larger than the second: $3 + 5 > 2 + 5$.

- You can add two numbers in either order: $6 + 3 = 3 + 6$.

- If you add an amount to one addend and subtract it from another addend, the sum remains the same: $6 + 6 = 12$; $7 + 5 = 12$.

- Addition and subtraction are related. If adding two numbers gives a certain sum, then subtracting one of the addends from the sum results in the other addend: $6 + 7 = 13$; $13 - 7 = 6$; $13 - 6 = 7$.

- You can break numbers into parts to add them: $6 + 8 = 6 + (4 + 4) = (6 + 4) + 4$.

- If you add two even numbers, the sum is even. If you add two odd numbers, the sum is even. If you add an even number and an odd number, the sum is odd.

Some of the generalizations investigated in Grades K–2 are revisited in Grades 3–5 with higher numbers and more complex problems. In addition, new general claims are investigated. Examples of general claims highlighted in Grades 3–5 are as follows:

- If you add the same amount to both numbers in a subtraction problem, the difference does not change: $145 - 97 = 148 - 100$.

- You can multiply two numbers in either order: $32 \times 20 = 20 \times 32$.

- You can break numbers into parts to multiply them, but each part of each number must be multiplied by each part of the other number: $7 \times 24 = 7 \times (20 + 4) = (7 \times 20) + (7 \times 4)$.

- Multiplication and division are related. If multiplying two numbers gives a certain product, then dividing that product by one of the original factors results in the other factor: $9 \times 8 = 72$; $72 \div 8 = 9$; $72 \div 9 = 8$.

- A factor of a number is a factor of multiples of that number: 3 is a factor of 15; 15 is a factor of 30, so 3 is a factor of 30.

- If you double (or triple) one of the factors in a multiplication problem and halve (or third) the other, the product remains the same: $164 \times 4 = 328 \times 2$.

Early Algebra: Patterns, Functions, and Change

Investigations includes a coherent K–5 strand on patterns, functions, and change, with one unit in each grade. The content of these units starts with repeating patterns and number sequences in Grades K and 1, connects these patterns and sequences to functional relationships beginning in Grade 2, and then develops ideas about linear and nonlinear contexts that involve relationships between two variables in Grades 3–5. In each of these units in K–5, the Algebra Connections essay highlights some of the ideas students work on in that unit, and how they connect to later work in algebra.

Patterns and Functions in Grades K–2

Work with repeating patterns has long been a staple of mathematics work in the primary grades, but it often seems to have little connection to work in later grades. In the *Investigations* sequence, students' study of the structure of repeating patterns is connected to work with ratios and linear functions by associating the repeating pattern with the counting numbers. Consider this example:

Students have been building repeating color patterns using connecting cubes. This red-blue-green repeating pattern has been numbered with the counting numbers, starting with 1. Students are considering which numbers are associated with the green cubes:

1 2 3 4 5 6 7 8 9 10 11 12

Kamala says that the greens have a "counting by 3s" pattern: 3, 6, 9, 12. Esperanza says, "it will always be on the threes because every time you skip two, then it's green." Theo adds, remembering a previous Investigation in which they built buildings from connecting cubes with the same number of cubes in each layer: "It's like the same pattern we made when we made the building. It's always adding threes. One floor is three, two floors is six, and you keep adding three—3, 6, 9, um, 12, and you keep going by 3s."

Students are recognizing the underlying 1:3 ratio in both situations. In the repeating pattern, there is a relationship between the position of each green cube among all green cubes and its position among all the cubes: the *first* green is in position 3 in the sequence, the *second* green in position 6, the *third* green in position 9, and so forth. In the cube building, there are 3 cubes for each floor: one floor has

3 cubes, 2 floors have 6 cubes, 3 floors have 9 cubes, and so forth. These constant ratio situations are students' first examples of linear change—change at a constant rate.

Examples of ideas investigated in Grades K–2 in these units are as follows:

- Repeating patterns can be described as iterations of a unit. This repeating color pattern can be divided into its units, the part that repeats:

- When the elements of a repeating pattern are numbered with the counting numbers, elements in the pattern can be characterized by a particular number sequence. In a red-blue-red-blue connecting cube train, the blue cubes are numbered 2, 4, 6, 8, . . . , and the red cubes are numbered 1, 3, 5, 7, ...

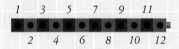

- The same number sequence can represent different situations. The blue cubes in a red-blue repeating pattern and the claps in a tap-clap repeating pattern fall in the same numbered positions.

- In a ratio situation, as one quantity changes by a certain amount, the other quantity always changes by a certain amount (for each day, there are 3 pennies added to the jar).

- Tables are a representation that can be used to show how one variable changes in relation to another.

- The same ratio relationship can occur in different contexts (e.g., 3 pennies per day, 3 cubes per "floor").

Patterns, Functions, and Change in Grades 3–5

In Grades 3–5, students focus on both linear and nonlinear change. Students study situations with a constant rate of change, in which two variables are related in ways that can be expressed in a verbal rule or an equation (such as the relationship between the total number of pennies in a jar and the number of days pennies have been collected, when a fixed number of pennies is added to the jar each day). They learn to take into account any starting amount (i.e., the number of pennies in the jar at the beginning) and the rate of change (i.e., the number of pennies added to the jar each day). They also study relationships in which the value of one variable cannot be determined based on the value of the other (such as the relationship between temperature and time in Grade 3 and between plant growth and time in Grade 4). In Grades 4 and 5, they also encounter situations in which the relationship between the two variables can be determined, but the change is not occurring at a constant rate, for example, a Penny Jar in which the number of pennies doubles each day.

Students work extensively with ways of representing relationships between two variables: with words, with tables and graphs, with numbers, and (starting in Grade 4) with symbolic notation. These units reinforce and connect with work in other units on multiplication, ratio, area, volume, and graphing. The Algebra Connections essay in each of the patterns, functions, and change units provides more detailed information about this sequence of students' work and how it connects to algebra.

Examples of ideas investigated in these units in Grades 3–5 (in addition to some of those in the K–2 list that continue to be studied in new contexts) are as follows:

- Line graphs are a representation that can show the relationship between two variables. A line graph represents both individual values of the variable and the rate of change of one variable in relation to another.

- In a situation with a constant rate of change, the value of one variable can be determined, given the value of the other.

- The relationship between two variables in a situation with a constant rate of change can be described in words and with symbolic notation.

- In some situations, the rate of change is determined but not constant. In these situations, the rate of change may be, for example, increasing by a constant amount.

Early Algebra Is Fundamental

Underlying the work in early algebra are, according to one of the *Investigations'* mathematician advisors, "foundational principles"—principles that connect elementary students' work in arithmetic to later work in algebra. For example, when second graders consider how changing the order of numbers in an addition or subtraction problem affects the sum or difference, they can engage in reasoning about foundational ideas, in this case, that addition is commutative, but subtraction is not: $a + b = b + a$, but $c - d \neq d - c$. Even though they may not yet have the experience with negative numbers to allow them to completely make sense of $14 - 26$, they see, through modeling and representing this problem, that it does not have the same difference as $26 - 14$. In later years, they will come to see that there *is* a regularity here, that if $c - d = a$, then $d - c = -a$, or $c - d = -(d - c)$.

Similarly, when fifth graders develop representations to show why halving one factor in a multiplication problem and doubling the other results in the same product, they are applying knowledge of foundational properties of multiplication and division. In later years, they may explain the more general claim that dividing one factor by any number (except 0) and multiplying the other factor by the same number maintains the same product by reference to the associative property of multiplication and to multiplication by 1—the identity element for multiplication. Through a series of steps, based on these properties of multiplication, one can show that, if a, b, and n are numbers $\left(n \neq 0 \right)$, then $a \times b = a \times b \times \frac{n}{n} = (a \times n) \times \left(\frac{b}{n} \right)$.

For most adults, notation such as the use of variables, operations, and equal signs is the chief identifying feature of algebra. Although students use symbolic notation in Grades 4 and 5, the notation is not the focus of activity in Grades K–5. Underlying the notation are ways of reasoning about how the operations work. This *reasoning* about how numbers can be put together and taken apart under different operations or about relationships between two changing quantities, *not* the notation, is the central work of elementary students in algebra.

Algebra for All Students

Work in early algebra in the elementary classroom has the potential of enhancing the learning of *all* students. The teachers with whom the *Investigations* team collaborated during the development of the curriculum commented on this potential in their classrooms. Teacher collaborators reported that students who tend to have difficulty in mathematics become stronger mathematical thinkers through this work. As one teacher wrote, "When I began to work on generalizations with my students, I noticed a shift in my less capable learners. Things seemed more accessible to them." When the generalizations are made explicit—through language and representations used to justify them—they become accessible to more students and can become the foundation for greater computational fluency. Furthermore, the disposition to create a representation when a mathematical question arises supports students in reasoning through their confusions.

At the same time, students who generally outperform their peers in mathematics find this content challenging and stimulating. The study of numbers and operations extends beyond efficient computation to the excitement of making and proving conjectures about mathematical relationships that apply to an infinite class of numbers. A teacher explained, "Students develop a habit of mind of looking beyond the activity to search for something more, some broader mathematical context to fit the experience into."

Early algebra is not an add-on. The foundations of algebra arise naturally throughout students' work with numbers, operations, and patterns and by using familiar and accessible contexts to investigate how one set of values changes in relation to another. This work anchors students' concepts of the operations and underlies greater computational flexibility.

Teacher Note

Discussing Mathematical Ideas

Throughout the *Investigations* curriculum, whole-class discussion is a key aspect of students' mathematical activity. Class discussion provides a time for students to

- articulate their mathematical ideas.

- share different approaches to solving a problem.

- identify and investigate what they don't understand.

- analyze why a solution works or how it is flawed.

- pose conjectures and identify evidence to support them.

- collaborate to build ideas or solve problems.

- develop mathematical language.

- use representations to describe mathematical relationships.

- compare and connect students' various ideas, representations, and solutions.

- learn to consider and question each other's ideas.

By carefully selecting problems, representations, and solutions for the whole class to consider, the teacher focuses discussion on key mathematical ideas and works with the class as a whole to move students' thinking forward.

Building a Mathematical Community

In the first weeks of school, teachers help the class develop norms for classroom discussion and work with students on attitudes and behavior that will support productive math discussions. Most teachers find that they need to work quite explicitly with students throughout the school year to first establish and then maintain expectations for class discussion. During discussions, teachers keep the flow of ideas organized and remind students about the appropriate focus. For example, "Right now I want comments that are either agreeing with, disagreeing with, or commenting on Yolanda's idea," or "So we now have three different approaches to this problem on the board. Is there a way in which Jill's is similar to Corey's?" Teachers also find opportunities to comment directly on student actions, behavior, and contributions that support productive discourse:

> Because Stephen was willing to talk through what was confusing him when he got an answer that he knew wasn't right, it seemed to really help all of us understand this kind of problem better.

> When Kamala put up her picture of the problem, I heard some of you say, "Ooh!" What was it you understood when you saw that picture? Did anyone else have a picture or a diagram that helped you understand how to solve this problem?

And from time to time teachers discuss directly with the class what aspects of class discussions have been helping or hindering students' participation:

> What helps you be willing to share your work or make an observation during class discussion? Are there times you don't feel comfortable speaking? Why is that?

Building an inclusive mathematics classroom involves a focus on respect for student ideas and acceptance of differences. Working on establishing this community with students will vary across grades and even from one year to another, depending on the needs and experiences of your students. (See the section "Setting Up the Mathematical Community" in Part 7, Working with the Range of Learners: Classroom Cases for some teachers' thoughts on building the classroom mathematics community.)

Focusing Class Discussions

Students' ideas are important and are, in fact, central to discussion. But if a discussion bounces among too many different ideas or tries to include too many different approaches, the discussion becomes ungrounded and hard for students to follow. Simply listing one problem-solving approach after another doesn't engage students beyond the few moments when they are contributing their own idea.

The Math Focus Points for Discussion and sample teacher dialogue found in the text for every discussion will help you guide the discussion. In preparing for class, ask yourself:

- What do I want this discussion to accomplish?

- What do I want all students to take away from this discussion?

- How will the time spent as a whole class enhance the work students have done individually or in pairs or groups?

During work that precedes the discussion, observe students' work with the upcoming discussion in mind. Ask yourself:

- What is a difficulty that many students are having?

- What is a problem that many students are struggling with?

- Is there a question that one pair or group came up with that it would be fruitful for the whole class to discuss?

- What are the basic approaches to solving this problem that students are using?

- Which students or groups have ideas or approaches that should be shared?

Student Participation

Whole-class discussion time is precious class time; it should serve to consolidate or move ahead the math thinking of all students. Find ways during discussions to elicit responses from different students. Although all students may not participate in any one discussion, all of your students' voices should be heard over the course of several discussions. There are many ways to work with students to encourage them to participate. For example, listen carefully to students' ideas and look carefully at their work during activities. Help particular students prepare to share one of their ideas. At first, some students might be more comfortable if you put their solution, representation, or idea on the board or a

transparency and present it to the class yourself; alternatively, the student might explain a certain part of the solution, while you add to the student's explanation.

Think of ways to invite all students' participation during each discussion by asking students to raise hands if they used the same approach or if they agree or disagree with a statement you or another student makes. Pose a question and have students discuss it for a few minutes in pairs before having the whole class consider it. Use wait time judiciously and think about ways that students can use quiet signals when they are ready to respond (e.g., thumbs up rather than hands waving); then students who are still thinking are not distracted.

Ideas are bound to come up that you cannot pursue during class discussions. Sometimes you cannot follow or decipher a student's idea at the moment or you are not sure about how it relates to what is being discussed. If you don't understand what a student is saying, you might ask another student to interpret or talk to the student later. Don't be afraid to let students know that you have to think about something and get back to them or follow up with them after the discussion. You can always bring an idea back to the class later if you decide it would be important for the class to think about it.

You can find other ways to follow up on a student's idea that is not central or accessible for the whole class: "I was thinking about your idea, and here's a problem I thought you could try it on." Some teachers have a "parking lot" poster for ideas that come up during class but they don't have time to pursue. These ideas may come up again later or can be referred to when they become relevant. The better you know the curriculum, the more you will know when they might come up.

Setting Up the Classroom for Discussion

It is critical that students are sitting in such a way that everyone is focused on the discussion and everyone can hear. If there are representations that students need to see during the discussions, they must be large enough and dark enough so that everyone can see them.

A variety of seating arrangements for class discussions can work, as long as there are clear expectations connected to them. In some classrooms, students gather on a rug for the class meeting and then return to their places or choose places for work time. In other classrooms, students often stay at their own desks for meetings. Some teachers vary the setting, with students staying at their desks when the meeting will be short and gathering together when a longer time is needed.

To facilitate a smooth transition to meeting on the rug, some teachers assign students places to sit on the rug, changing them every month or so. Others place circles, mats, or white boards to clearly mark the places available for students to sit. Others allow students to sit wherever they want in a circle as long as they can see the teacher and all of the other students. They might remind students to make a good choice about sitting in a position and next to classmates that enables them to focus on the discussion. While some students can pay attention while sitting on the floor, others do better in a chair.

Guidelines for Whole-Class Discussions

In summary, here are some guidelines to keep in mind for your class's whole-group discussions:

- Set up norms and review them frequently; point out examples in which they are working.

- Plan a clear purpose and focus for each discussion, based on the listed Focus Points.

- Use wait time to give students time to think.

- Ask students to use quiet student signals to indicate they are ready to respond.

- Prepare with some students ahead of time to participate in the discussion.

- Have clear visuals that everyone can see and refer to.

- Establish a routine arrangement that ensures that everyone can hear and see.

- Select only a few students to share solutions.

When all students come to a discussion prepared to listen actively and to contribute ideas, the class discussions provide an important forum in which they can articulate, represent, connect, and consolidate the mathematical ideas they have been working on.

Racial and Linguistic Diversity in the Classroom: What Does Equity Mean in Today's Math Classroom?

… we have no patterns for relating across our human differences as equals. As a result, those differences have been misnamed and misused in the service of separation and confusion.[1]

Audre Lorde

We must not, in trying to think about how we can make a big difference, ignore the small daily differences we can make which, over time, add up to big differences that we often cannot foresee.[2]

Marian Wright Edelman

U.S. public schools are responsible for educating students who are more racially and linguistically diverse than at any other time in our history. The beginning of the 21st century in the United States is marked by an influx of immigrants, and schools and teachers are at the front door meeting these students. Hence, many teachers work in classrooms with increasing numbers of immigrant students, students of color, and linguistically diverse students who often face unique challenges related to language proficiency, cultural and social adaptation, and poverty. What are the issues and challenges for teachers in these diverse classrooms?

While developing this curriculum, the *Investigations* staff and field-test teachers worked together to continue educating ourselves about this question. Many of us have had direct experience teaching in schools where students come from diverse racial, cultural, and linguistic backgrounds. In many cases, the students' culture, race, ethnicity, and first language are different from those of the teacher. This Teacher Note provides a glimpse into the complex issues about racial,

cultural, and linguistic diversity being discussed in the field of education today. It also provides resources for further reading, including those we found helpful in our own professional development.

Equity in the Mathematics Classroom

Equity does not mean that every student should receive identical instruction; instead, it demands that reasonable and appropriate accommodations be made as needed to promote access and attainment for all students. (NCTM, 2000, p. 11)

Investigations was developed with the assumption that all learners can engage in challenging and substantive mathematics. Assumptions about students' capacity and inclination to learn in school can undermine their access to and participation in significant mathematics learning. An extensive body of literature documents the persistence of these assumptions and their effects on students' opportunity to learn. For example, students of color and those whose first language is not English are often seen in terms of what they lack instead of what they bring to the learning environment (termed in the literature a *deficit thinking* model). Student underperformance in school may be explained by student and family shortcomings, behavior that does not match a particular set of norms, immaturity, or lack of intelligence. Students who do not speak fluent English may be judged as having poor or underdeveloped conceptual understanding because they cannot yet express the complexity of their thinking in English. Misunderstanding cultural differences can lead schools to inappropriately place children into special education and low-ability groups and to expect less from them than from other children. For instance, Entwistle and Alexander (1989) report that poor black children are often described as less mature, and, consequently, school personnel may hold lower expectations for them than for children whose socioeconomic status is higher.

---

[1] From a paper delivered at the Copeland Colloquium, Amherst College, in April, 1980. The paper was entitled, "Age, Race, Class, and Sex: Women Redefining Difference."

[2] Marian Wright Edelman, "Families in Peril: An Agenda for Social Change," The W. E. B. Du Bois Lectures (Cambridge, Mass.: Harvard University Press, 1987), p. 107.

Many teachers are working hard to improve learning opportunities for these students, with the goal of enhancing both the learning climate and students' educational performance. In this work, teachers must consider the broader issues as well as practices, procedures, strategies, and other key aspects of schooling. In an educational setting, equity indicates a state in which all children—students of color and white students, males and females, successful students and those who have fallen behind, and students who have been denied access in the past—have equal opportunities to learn, participate in challenging programs, and have equal access to the services they need to benefit from that education. Equity has sometimes been oversimplified to mean that all students should be treated the same—neutrally and without differentiation. Rather, differences matter, and matter in specific ways. Successful learning experiences depend on teachers building on the contributions of all students and recognizing the differences that matter to them.

In the mathematics education literature, researchers from four projects, three in the United States and one in South Africa, looked across their projects to identify features of classrooms "essential for supporting students' understanding" in mathematics (Hiebert et al., 1997). They organize these in five dimensions, one of which is "equity and accessibility." The authors describe this dimension as fundamental:

> [E]quity . . . is not an add-on or an optional dimension. It is an integral part of a system of instruction that sets students' understanding of mathematics as the goal. Without equity, the other dimensions are restricted and the system does not function well. (p. 12)

Race and Linguistic Diversity

While teaching a seminar on race in education several years ago, one of the authors of this essay was met with a remarkable silence and little open discussion of race, racism, and the ways they come up in classroom teaching. Some think that racism is no longer an issue in schools, and that "color blindness" is the way to approach a diverse class of students. However, many in the field believe that explicit classroom attention to race, ethnicity, and home language results in increased communication and learning.

Race (or ethnicity) can have overlapping and coexisting categories of meaning. Sometimes, race signifies being economically, socially, politically, and educationally oppressed. Other times it signifies a sense of community and belonging, involving valuable associations with a particular group, history, cultural codes, and sensibilities. Race conveys multiple meanings, and racism takes on multiple forms, subject to context and situation. Whether expressed subtly or with crude directness, the effects of racism are felt in everyday school experience. Preconceptions about who students are, which are based on surface behaviors, can mask important potential.

For example, in one classroom, a Hmong girl is quiet, well behaved, and does little to demand attention. But although she is well behaved, she is not engaged and does not quite know what's going on in the lesson. In another classroom, a young black boy is distracted and disruptive, eager to contribute, but often "in trouble." The Hmong girl might be seen as a model student—quiet, hard working, high achieving, and nonchallenging of classroom norms. In contrast, the black boy might be seen as loud, threatening, noncompliant, dysfunctional, and low achieving. The characterization of the Hmong girl seems positive, even flattering, in comparison to the characterization of the black boy. However, both views may be silencing the voices, needs, and potential contributions of these children in different ways. For the Hmong girl, a focus on seemingly compliant behavior may lead the teacher to ignore her educational needs. For the black boy, a focus on seemingly bad behavior may distract the teacher from recognizing his educational strengths.

To understand all students' experiences—to support them in rigorous learning and to respect the variety of their language practices, histories, and identities—educators must continue to learn about the issues of race and racism, cultural and linguistic diversity, and teaching practices and strategies that support the learning of all students.

Teaching Practices and Strategies

Many important insights about teaching practices and strategies that support students of color and English language learners can be gleaned from those who have been studying and writing in the field. Some of these educators and researchers focus specifically on the mathematics classroom, but there are also accounts from science and literacy that have a great deal to offer the teaching of mathematics.

Gloria Ladson-Billings studied exemplary teachers of African-American students and has written about an approach of "culturally relevant teaching." Although the teachers she studied differed in the way they structured their classrooms—some appeared more "traditional," while others were more "progressive" in their teaching strategies—their conceptions of and beliefs about teaching and learning had many commonalities. Here is a subset of characteristics of these teachers adapted from Ladson-Billings' list (1995). These teachers:

- believed that all students are capable of academic success.

- saw their pedagogy as always in process.

- developed a community of learners.

- encouraged students to learn collaboratively and be responsible for each other.

- believed that knowledge is shared, recycled, and constructed.

- believed they themselves must be passionate about learning.

- believed they must scaffold, or build bridges, to facilitate learning.

- believed assessment must be multifaceted.

Overall, these teachers supported their students and held them to high standards:

> Students were not permitted to choose failure in their classrooms. They cajoled, nagged, pestered, and bribed

the students to work at high intellectual levels. Absent from their discourse was the "language of lacking." . . . Instead, teachers talked about their own shortcomings and limitations and ways they needed to change to ensure student success. (p. 479)

Critical to teaching students who bring a variety of cultural, social, and linguistic experience into the classroom is what Marilyn Cochran-Smith (1995b) calls "understanding children's understanding":

> [C]entral to learning to teach in a culturally and linguistically diverse society is understanding children's understanding or exploring what it means to know a child, to consider his or her background, behaviors, and interactions with others, and to try to do what Duckworth calls "give reason" to the ways the child constructs meanings and interpretations, drawing on experiences and knowledge developed both inside and outside the classroom. (p. 511)

Eleanor Duckworth, whom Cochran-Smith cites above, may have originated the phrase *understanding children's understanding* in her essay of the same name (1996). In that essay, she discusses the idea of "giving children reason" as she describes a group of teachers in a study group who set themselves this challenge: "[E]very time a child did or said something whose meaning was not immediately obvious . . . [they] sought to understand the way in which . . . [it] could be construed to make sense" (pp. 86–87).

This work of hearing and understanding students' ideas, discourse, and representations and involving all of them in significant intellectual work can be especially challenging when students come from backgrounds quite different from the teacher's own. Cindy Ballenger's *Teaching Other People's Children* (1999) and Vivian Paley's *White Teacher* (1989) provide first-person accounts of teachers who are actively examining their own preconceptions about the behavior and discourse of the students they teach. Ballenger expresses how her initial belief that all students could learn was not enough:

I began with these children expecting deficits, not because I believed they or their background was deficient—I was definitely against such a view—but because I did not know how to see their strengths . . . I came to see . . . strengths . . . that are part of an intellectual tradition, not always a schooled tradition, but an intellectual one nonetheless, and one that, therefore, had a great deal to say to teaching and learning. (p. 3)

Ballenger recounts her journey in learning to listen to the sense of her students, both "honoring the child's home discourse" and engaging the student in "school-based and discipline-based ways of talking, acting, and knowing" (p. 6).

Working in English with students whose first language is not English presents two challenges to teachers who do not share the student's first language: (1) how to learn about, respect, and support the discourse practices that students can contribute from their own knowledge and communities; and (2) how to bring students into the language of the discipline of mathematics in English. Judit Moschkovich (1999) identifies two critical functions of mathematical discussions for English language learners: "uncovering the mathematical content in student contributions and bringing different ways of talking and points of view into contact" (p. 11). She identifies several important instructional strategies that support these students' participation in math discussions (p. 11):

• using several expressions for the same concept

• using gestures and objects to clarify meaning

• accepting and building on student responses

• revoicing student statements with more technical terms

• focusing not only on vocabulary development but also on mathematical content and argumentation practices

Josiane Hudicourt-Barnes (2003) writes about the participation of students whose home language is Haitian Creole. Her research highlights the way that understanding the forms of discourse students contribute from their own culture enables teachers to uncover and appreciate how students are making sense of subject matter. Although she writes about science learning, her observations are applicable to the mathematics classroom: "To be 'responsive to the children and responsible to the subject matter' (Ball, 1997, p. 776), we must be able to hear children's diverse voices and create opportunities for them to pursue their ideas and questions (p. 17)." Further, she argues that classroom discourse that follows a rigid, restrictive format "may mean that children from families of non-Western traditions are shut out of classroom participation and that skills from other traditions are devalued and subtracted from children's cognitive repertoires, and therefore also made unavailable to their fellow students" (p. 17).

Being "responsive to the children and responsive to the subject matter" is highlighted by many of the writers in this field. They emphasize that the teacher's responsibility is *both* to the students' ideas, sense making, and forms of discourse *and* to bringing these students in to the ideas, vocabulary, and ways of working in the discipline of the content area. Gloria Ladson-Billings (2002) sums up her observations of a teacher whose urban, largely African American, students, initially hated writing:

To meet the academic goals he had set, Carter had to rethink his practice in some fundamental ways. . . . He had to keep a sense of uncertainty and a willingness to question in the forefront of his teaching. . . . while Carter empathized with the students' struggle to write he understood that his job was to teach them to do it. He didn't put them down for not enjoying writing or writing well, but he also did not let them off the hook. He had to help them appreciate the power and fulfillment of writing and he had to preserve each student's sense of self. (p. 118)

Continuing to Learn

Continuing to learn is something we all can do. This Teacher Note attempts only to introduce you to some authors and resources who can contribute to that learning. Many of the resources cited here include rich examples from classrooms that can evoke productive interaction when read and discussed with peers. You may have opportunities to take advantage of courses, seminars, or study groups, such as the one that Lawrence and Tatum (1997) describe, or to self-organize peer discussions of articles in the field.

Teachers can also pose their own questions and study their own classrooms. Writing brief case studies in which you raise your own questions about these issues in your teaching and then sharing your writing can be a rich source of learning. You might start by reading what other teachers have written about their own practice as they reflect on their teaching of diverse students. For example, in *What's Happening in Math Class?* (Schifter, 1996), Alissa Sheinbach writes about three students who are struggling in mathematics (vol. 1, pp. 115–129), Allen Gagnon writes about his Spanish-speaking students (vol. 1, pp. 129–136), and Nora Toney recounts her own experiences with racism as a student (when she was bused into a largely white school) and later as a teacher herself (vol. 2, pp. 26–36). After describing some successful experiences in mathematics she had as an adult that contrasted with her experience in the "low group" as a student, Toney concludes by identifying factors that have been important to her own learning:

> I have discovered the ingredients necessary for me to learn and achieve success: high teacher expectation, fairness, inclusiveness, engaging contextual material, constant monitoring and feedback, discussions/debates, and reflective writing. Generally speaking, I need numerous opportunities to connect my thinking and ideas to new concepts and ideas. These factors facilitated my *learning* of mathematics, so now I am trying to incorporate these same factors into *teaching* mathematics. (p. 36)

References and Additional Readings

Ball, D. (1997). What do students know? Facing challenges of distance, context, and desire in trying to hear children. In T. Biddle, T. Good, & I. Goodson (Eds.), *International handbook on teachers and teaching* (pp. 769–817). Dordrecht, Netherlands: Kluwer Press.

Ballenger, C. (1999). *Teaching other people's children: Literacy and learning in a bilingual classroom.* New York: Teachers College Press.

Cochran-Smith, M. (1995a). Uncertain allies: Understanding the boundaries of race and teaching. *Harvard Educational Review,* 63, 541–570.

Cochran-Smith, M. (1995b). Color blindness and basket making are not the answers: Confronting the dilemmas of race, culture, and language diversity in teacher education. *American Educational Research Journal,* 32, 493–522.

Duckworth, E. (1996). *"The having of wonderful ideas" and other essays on teaching and learning.* New York: Teachers College Press.

Entwistle, D., and Alexander, K. (1989). Early schooling as a "critical period" phenomenon. In K. Namboodiri & R. Corwin (Eds.), *Research in Sociology of Education and Socialization,* Volume 8, (pp. 27–55) Greenwich, CT: Jai Press.

Heath, S. B. (1983). *Ways with words: Language, life, and work in communities and classrooms.* New York: Cambridge University Press.

Hiebert, J., Carpenter, T. P., Fennema, E., Fuson, K. C., Wearne, D., Murray, H., et al. (1997). *Making sense: Teaching and learning mathematics with understanding.* Portsmouth, NH: Heinemann.

Hudicourt-Barnes, J. (2003). The use of argumentation in Haitian Creole science classrooms. *Harvard Educational Review,* 73(1), 73–93.

King, J. (1991). Dysconscious racism: Ideology, identity, and the miseducation of teachers. *The Journal of Negro Education,* 60, 133–146.

Ladson-Billings, G. (1994). *The dreamkeepers: Successful teaching for African American students.* San Francisco: Jossey-Bass.

Ladson-Billings, G. (1995). Toward a theory of culturally relevant pedagogy. *American Educational Research Journal,* 32, 465–491.

Ladson-Billings, G. (2002). I ain't writin' nuttin': Permission to fail and demands to succeed in urban classrooms. In L. Delpit & J. K. Dowdy (Eds.), *The skin that we speak: Thoughts on language and culture in the classroom* (pp. 107–120). New York: The New Press.

Lawrence, S. M., & Tatum, B. D. (1997). White educators as allies: Moving from awareness to action. In M. Fine, L. Weis, L. C. Powell, & L. M. Wong (Eds.), *Off white: Readings on race, power, and society* (pp. 333–342). New York: Routledge.

Lewis, A. (2003). *Race in the schoolyard: Negotiating the color line in classrooms and communities.* New Brunswick, New Jersey and London: Rutgers University Press.

Moschkovich, J. (1999). Supporting the participation of English language learners in mathematical discussions. *For the Learning of Mathematics,* 19(1), 11–19.

National Council of Teachers of Mathematics. (2000). *Principles and standards for school mathematics.* Reston, VA: Author.

Obidah, J., & Teel, K. M. (1996). The impact of race on cultural differences on the teacher/student relationship: A collaborative classroom study by an African American and Caucasian teacher research team. *Kansas Association for Supervision and Curriculum Development Record,* 14, 70–86.

Obidah, J., & Teel, K. M. (2001). *Because of the kids.* New York: Teachers College Press.

Paley, V. G. (1989). *White teacher.* Cambridge, MA: Harvard University Press.

Schifter, D. (1996). *What's happening in math class? Vol. 1: Envisioning new practices through teacher narratives ; Vol. 2: Reconstructing professional identities.* New York: Teachers College Press.

Titles of Kindergarten Teacher Notes by Unit

Unit 5 Make a Shape, Build a Block

Unit 6 How Many Do You Have?

Unit 7 Sorting and Surveys

PART 7

Working with the Range of Learners

Preview

All teachers are faced with the challenge of meeting the needs of a range of learners in their classrooms. The range of learners can include students who struggle in certain areas of mathematics, those who excel in math, students who are English Language Learners, and students who have particular learning needs.

This section contains a series of case studies written by Kindergarten teachers from urban, suburban, and rural schools, telling how they implemented the *Investigations* program in their classrooms. The students in these classrooms vary on many dimensions, including gender, language, culture and ethnicity, and special needs. They present a range of strengths and needs in their prior experience with mathematics and their confidence in the classroom.

Through their writing, these teachers bring us into their classrooms and invite us to participate in how they think about supporting their range of learners. As they captured moments in time in their classrooms, the teachers did not intend to provide exemplary actions to be emulated or a how-to manual of what to do for particular students or with particular activities. Rather, they offer the kind of thinking teachers do as a matter of course in their teaching. Through the hundreds of interactions they have with their students each day, teachers try to understand what those students bring to their learning and how to support them in moving further. In these case studies, they share some of that thinking.

We collected these cases together in this book, rather than including them with the curriculum units, because they are not designed to illustrate "how to do" a particular activity. Rather, as a group, they provide examples and questions to inspire your own questioning and reflection. You may want to use this set of cases on your own or discuss them with a group of colleagues.

Keep in mind that each case provides only a glimpse into a teacher's classroom. Just as you would not expect anyone to understand the complexity of the issues you face in your own classroom from such a brief glimpse, the cases cannot provide all the background information you might need to understand a particular teacher's decision with a particular student on a particular day. But you do not need to know more detail to use these cases for your own professional development. Use them as starting points when considering similar issues that you face with your students. The questions at the end of each case provide a starting point for discussion. If you discuss these cases with colleagues in a cross-grade group, you will have even more examples to consider by combining the sets of cases from two or more grades.

The classroom cases are grouped into three themes, focusing on some of the most important issues teachers face as they work to meet the needs of their students. In the first section, "Setting Up the Mathematical Community," teachers write about how they create a supportive and productive learning environment in their classrooms. In the second section, "Accommodations for Learning," teachers focus on specific modifications they make to meet the needs of some of their learners. Because these teachers chose to write about particular students in their classrooms, the cases do not cover all the kinds of needs and accommodations you might encounter. However, even though the specific students discussed may differ from students in your own classroom, these teachers consistently found that accommodations they had made for one student often spilled over to benefit other students with related needs. In the last section, "Language and Representation," teachers share how they help students use representations and develop language to investigate and express mathematical ideas.

There is, of course, much overlap. Some cases illustrate ideas that could fall into more than one of these sections. You will find ideas from one section cropping up in the cases in other sections. For example, when teachers develop accommodations for learning, they are often using mathematical representations or helping students connect their language to the mathematical ideas.

Note: Pseudonyms have been used for all student and teacher names.

Summary of Cases

Setting Up the Mathematical Community

Getting Started: Using the *Calendar* Routine to Develop a Math Community

Michelle Rutherford uses the *Calendar* routine as one occasion for her students to learn about how to participate in a mathematical community.

Supporting Student Participation in Discussions

Carolejo Li works with her students to create a mathematical community in which students are able to share ideas and learn from each other.

Accommodations for Learning

Linus: The Journey Begins

This is the first of three cases that follow Linus, a student in Samantha MacDonald's class, on his journey to adjust both academically and socially to Kindergarten.

Linus: Building Numbers Greater Than 4

Samantha MacDonald designs a game to help Linus and other students in her class model quantities represented by written numerals.

It's Like a Cheer: Linus's Journey Continues

In the last case in the series, Linus's growth is evident as he makes a contribution to a mathematical discussion about patterns.

Change It: How Students Adapt Activities

Samantha MacDonald finds that an accommodation made for one student meets the needs of her range of learners in unexpected ways.

How Many Students Are in Our Class?

Meghan Mallon shares a data activity that meets the needs of all her learners while providing an extra challenge for some of her students.

Language and Representation

Sharing Marbles: Representing and Solving a Division Problem

The students in Susan Sharrow's class use the mathematical skills they have developed over the year to represent and solve a new type of problem.

Reflections on *Collect 10 Together*

Through reflection and redirection, Meghan Mallon makes the goals of *Collect 10 Together* more explicit for herself and her students.

"Heptagons" and Twins

Samantha MacDonald finds that the ideas in the geometry unit are accessible to all of her learners.

The Red One Doesn't Have a Match: A Counting Jar Discussion

Michelle Rutherford creates an experience that stretches her students to think about odd numbers.

How Do You Draw the Ones That Are Gone? Showing the Action of a Subtraction Problem

A few of Susan Sharrow's students create a visual representation of a subtraction story problem and share their ideas with the class.

Helping Students Build on Each Other's Ideas

Meghan Mallon encourages her students to experiment with the mathematical ideas raised by two of their classmates.

Setting Up the Mathematical Community

Getting Started: Using the *Calendar* Routine to Develop a Math Community

Creating a classroom culture that allows students to share ideas, listen to, and learn from each other takes a great deal of thought and work on the part of the teacher. These skills and practices develop over time. The first month of school is when teachers begin to establish the classroom atmosphere that they would like to see unfold throughout the year. In this case, Michelle Rutherford reflects on her thoughts at the beginning of the school year.

There is much on my mind each September as the school bell rings for the first time, when a new set of 5- and 6-year-olds gathers in front of me on their first day of Kindergarten. I wonder, "Who are these students? What new adventures await us? Will I be able to excite their imaginations and their quest for knowledge and independence? How will I meet their needs socially, academically, and cognitively? What will be our successes this year? What will be our biggest challenge?" As I take a deep breath and begin my greeting, one thing is for sure, I have felt these feelings before; no matter how long I have been a Kindergarten teacher, I know the days ahead will be full of bursts of successes, some frustrations, and enlightenment for both myself and my students.

From our initial conversations in using the calendar and in taking attendance, I can tell that this group of students is eager to share what they know about numbers. The calendar is a focal point in the Kindergarten classroom, as many of my students are already familiar with it from their work in preschool. Students chime right in as I sing our days of the week song and are bursting at the seams to tell me what number they think is showing on the calendar for today. I feel like I have barely taken hold of the reins, and we are off and running at full speed. When I ask the students what they notice about the calendar, many seem energized by the question. Some are shouting out answers, others are eagerly waving their hands in the air, while still others seem silenced by all the commotion.

Jackie says aloud, "I see a 6." I also hear Evan, "I have a calendar at my house. My birthday is in October. I am going to be 6." At the same time Sandy turns to Janice, "I had fun at your birthday party." The conversation is spontaneous, but I fear it may get away from us. Talk of birthdays can do this in a Kindergarten. While these vocal students are chiming in with enthusiasm, I see Carl, Will, Pat, and Debbie sitting more removed from the group. At the same time, Mike's body is in constant motion, and Sharon looks like she may cry. I know that she already misses her family. How do all these students feel in this new place? Do they seem removed, anxious, or scared because they are unsure of what is expected? Is this an indication of their overall disposition to learning? It is so important to make room for all learners from the very first day.

I want so much to capture the natural curiosity and tap into the mathematical instincts of these Kindergartners. At the same time, my goal is to set the expectation that everyone has a role in these discussions and to develop a sense of responsibility toward self and others. These students seem so alive while talking about numbers and the calendar. All at once I want to know everything they know and think about numbers, but then I realize we have only been in school 15 minutes. How can I harness this positive energy, while making room for those students whom I can tell are already overwhelmed by this level of intensity around learning? One thing I know for sure: I need to quickly and consistently establish some expectations for who we are as a class, for learning and sharing, and for listening and speaking. I also know that our daily routines are opportunities to work on these expectations.

I use the *Calendar* routine as a time to focus on helping students build relationships with each other and engage in mathematics thinking and learning. Working as a whole class on the *Calendar* routine allows the tension that some students feel to come to the surface very quickly so that we can recognize it and begin to deal with it. I model how the routine works the first three days; then I select one helper per day to facilitate the routine for the class. Each day the helper leads the class in our days of the week song and then determines which number comes next on the calendar as a way of determining the date.

By having one helper per day, the students come to anticipate that they will each get a turn and to recognize that they are expected to participate. The verbally precocious students learn to share the stage. The more reserved students learn that they are expected to take a turn, and that I am there, along with their classmates, to support them if they are hesitant, uncertain, or confused. Over time, the familiarity of the routine helps to ease the minds of those who are anxious.

Working with students on the *Calendar* routine seems so simple, but it is an important first step for setting a tone of inclusion, respect, and responsibility. The kinds of conversations that begin with our focus on the calendar also help my students learn that we will be talking a lot about numbers and math concepts in this class.

Michelle Rutherford uses the daily Calendar *routine as a time to model her expectations for what participating in a mathematics community will entail, both mathematically and socially. By doing so, she helps her students develop the skills they will need to become mathematically powerful thinkers who are able to listen to the ideas of others and to explain their own strategies and ideas.*

Questions for Discussion

1. As Ms. Rutherford observes her students' participation in the *Calendar* routine, what concerns does she express about the range of learners in her classroom? What specific skills does she believe all students will need to grow together as a mathematics community? How does she use this routine to help all students develop these skills?

2. What specific activities do you focus on at the beginning of the year to model your expectations for the type of community you wish to establish in your classroom?

Supporting Student Participation in Discussions

To create a classroom community in which learners are able to communicate effectively with each other, teachers must support their students' participation in mathematical discussions. Educational researchers in mathematics suggest that teachers enhance meaningful participation in mathematical discussions by

- *encouraging student conjectures.*

- *asking for explanations and evidence from students.*

- *focusing on the process of problem solving and the reasoning behind it.*

- *providing students with opportunities to compare methods, solutions, and explanations.*

- *engaging students in developing arguments to support their mathematical statements.*

- *asking students to paraphrase each other's statements and structuring activities so that students seek to understand each other's methods.*

Carolejo Li, a Kindergarten teacher, begins the year with many of these ideas in mind. Here she describes her efforts to create a mathematical community in which all learners participate and are able to listen to and build on each other's ideas.

Creating a math community in a Kindergarten classroom is challenging yet rewarding. One strategy I use in my classroom is to develop a discussion format that allows me to include and validate all of my students' ideas. I see these discussions as essential for bringing out the mathematics in the *Investigations* activities. I also see them as essential in helping students learn how to communicate their own mathematical thinking. This communication piece is a big part of helping my students see themselves as mathematicians and a big part of helping our class become a community of mathematicians.

One of my first conversations every year is about counting. Every morning we count the students in our class to determine how many students came to school that day. At the beginning of the year, there are always some students who don't apply one-to-one correspondence yet. Also, some students can count accurately when they are doing the counting, but when they observe another student who does not use one-to-one correspondence, they don't quite see where the inaccuracy comes from.

One year I decided to have a conversation about counting. I started with a simple question, "What is counting?" I really wasn't sure what I would get in response, but I decided to try it and hoped I would be able to shape the conversation into something valuable for everyone. Over the years I have restructured this discussion and now it goes something like this: I count the students that day as usual, but I do it wrong (usually without one-to-one correspondence). The students all react quite strongly. Then I let them describe what I am doing (they love to do that) and what I need to do to count accurately.

Somehow this discussion ends up being one where the students don't have to raise hands and everyone listens to each other. Ideally, I would like this to happen for all of our discussions. I feel that the best conversations that we have in my classroom are the ones that just flow—no one has to raise a hand to speak and everyone listens to each other. In fact, at times my interjections are minimal.

Because counting is our first discussion of the year, I make sure anyone who wants to say something has an opportunity to do so and that every idea is validated in some way. This conversation sets the tone that one of the things we talk about in our classroom is math and that everyone has important thoughts to contribute.

Another type of mathematical discussion we have is based on the question "What do you notice?" I use this question to launch a new activity or to wrap it up. I love asking this question because there are no wrong answers, and I am often very surprised by how sophisticated my students' observations can be. Initially, I get more responses than I would with a more specific question that has a correct answer. As time goes on, I often get almost the whole class raising hands to respond to this question. I think that my students feel safe in these discussions because they realize that their ideas are important. I try to be very careful about how I respond to their observations and do so in a nonjudgmental manner. I usually repeat or rephrase what a student offers. I often ask if anyone wants to respond to an observation. Sometimes I will just make a list of observations. Most of the time we will launch from an observation into a discussion about the observation. I believe the last of these approaches helps my students feel like their ideas are valuable. A student or a group of students offers an observation, and then we have a rich discussion centered on that observation.

I feel that creating a class of students who can share observations, share strategies, and discuss topics—all centered around math— is a process. We are always working to hone our communication skills in this manner, but in the end we look back in amazement at all the math we have learned over the year.

In this case, Ms. Li shares how she begins the process of teaching her students to participate in mathematical discussions. Her strategies include planning discussions that flow from open-ended questions and facilitating conversations that encourage student-to-student talk. Ms. Li recognizes that the art of successful mathematical discussions develops over time. As the year goes on, she continues to engage her students in mathematical conversations, giving them plenty of opportunity to practice and build on the important skills they are learning.

Questions for Discussion

1. **How does Ms. Li's use of open-ended questions like "What do you notice?" help foster a supportive environment for discussion in her classroom? What other strategies does she use to help her students develop into a community of math thinkers?**

2. **In what ways do you foster conversations in a whole-group setting? How do your strategies help all students feel they are a valued and important part of the mathematics community in your classroom?**

Accommodations for Learning

Linus: The Journey Begins

Each year teachers encounter a new group of learners with varying strengths and abilities. This makes it important for teachers to spend time at the beginning of the year closely observing their students to gain a sense of where these students are as learners. In this case, Kindergarten teacher Samantha MacDonald focuses on Linus, a student who is having a difficult time adjusting to the emotional and academic demands of Kindergarten. During the first weeks of school, Ms. MacDonald observes and interacts with Linus to learn more about what he knows and can do. This information will help her design the work she needs to do with Linus in the months to come. Here Ms. MacDonald describes Linus's behavior at the start of school.

From the first day of school, I could tell that Linus was not feeling very sure about his new class and the set of expectations that accompany coming to Kindergarten. In moments of confusion or commotion, he would find comfort in sucking his thumb. When a new task was introduced to the class, he often asked, "Will this be long?"

After watching Linus's participation in two daily math routines, Ms. MacDonald realizes that his apprehension may have to do with his limited number sense. As Linus participates in the activity Counting Around the Circle *(part of the attendance routine), she notices that he has trouble with the counting sequence beyond the number 5. She also notices that Linus calls out 18 at the end of the count, regardless of how many students are present. Here Ms. MacDonald describes his participation in another number activity—The Counting Jar.*

The *Counting Jar* activity brought up another challenge for Linus. I began the activity by placing three apples in the jar. All of my students seemed to recognize right away that there were three apples in the jar and did not find it necessary to count to confirm the total. Next, I passed out a plastic plate to each student and set out bear counters, connecting cubes, and color tiles. I asked them to use the tools I had set out to make an equivalent set of items on their plate. When they completed the task, they returned to our meeting area. With one glance around the circle, I could tell that most of my students made sense of the task and were quickly successful.

However, 4 of the 18 students had more than three items on their plates. Linus was one of them. I called the students back together to discuss the problem.

I asked the students to each explain what they did to solve this problem. When it was Linus's turn to share, he said, "I don't remember." Keeping in mind Linus's emotional tenuousness, I decided to move on. I felt tense as I tried to meet Linus's need while I simultaneously encouraged the next student to share.

Later, I asked Linus to do the *Counting Jar* activity with me individually. He was sure there were three apples in the jar. He counted them without taking the apples out of the jar. However, when it came to creating an equivalent set, he grabbed a handful of bear counters and dropped them on his plate without counting.

Teacher: How many bears do you have?

Linus: I don't know [thumb quickly moves to his mouth].

Teacher: How can you find out?

Linus: [quickly removing his thumb as he spoke] I can count.

With this, Linus began to randomly touch a bear and say the counting sequence. When he got to 10, he repeated 6, then said 7, 8, 10, 16, 4, 7, and 2. His number naming was as random as his pointing to the objects. As a signal for him to stop, I placed my hand over his. He did. Instantly his thumb went back in his mouth.

Teacher: How many bears do you have?

Linus: I don't know. Three?

Teacher: How many apples are in the jar?

Linus: Three.

Teacher: Do you have the same number of bears as apples?

Linus: No.

Teacher: Why not?

Linus: [pointing to the bears] These are more.

We stopped our conversation, and Linus went happily on to another activity with his friends. Our quick conversation had helped me to see the kinds of goals I need to put in place for Linus. Rote counting to 20 and beyond, one-to-one correspondence of a given set of objects, and establishing the purpose of counting to determine a quantity—these were all benchmark phrases that clicked through my mind to create an instructional map. The statements were clear, but what do they mean for right now and how do they help us move into the future? So many questions, and most pressing, as in every year, I wonder, how do we get from here to there with meaning and grace?

At the beginning of the year, Ms. MacDonald observes all her students carefully to assess their understanding of and facility with numbers. She assesses Linus during whole group activities, and then meets with him individually to help her understand more about his number knowledge and his approach to solving problems.

Questions for Discussion

1. What did Ms. MacDonald discover about what Linus does and does not understand about counting?

2. What goals does she have in mind for Linus in the area of counting? What could she now plan to support the development of Linus's counting skills?

3. What are ways you informally assess your students' counting skills at the beginning of the year? What experiences do you plan to help students develop these skills?

Linus: Building Numbers Greater Than 4

Two months have passed since Ms. MacDonald first wrote about Linus, a Kindergarten student who was having a hard time adjusting to the emotional and academic demands of school. Although Linus now appears to be more comfortable in school, his number concepts continue to lag far behind those of his classmates.

Ms. MacDonald has noticed that Linus has selected the game Compare *as his choice several days in a row. She observes that Linus is eager to play the game and has no trouble participating when the number on the card is less than or equal to 4. When the number on his card is greater than 4, however, Ms. MacDonald notices that Linus waits quietly until his partner supplies the correct answer. This brief session prompts Ms. MacDonald to design a new game* to encourage Linus to develop strategies for determining the quantity on the card and to push him to work with numbers higher than 4.*

After observing Linus, I realized that I needed to design a new activity to encourage more active participation from all students when playing the game *Compare*. I decided to introduce the class to a new game I developed—*Build It*. My purpose in designing this game was to take a situation that was already somewhat routine and comfortable for Linus and finesse a way to force him to attend to each number presented on the cards. I felt other students could also benefit from this modification. The focus on number recognition and establishing a quantity remained, though the focus on comparing one number to another temporarily took a back seat. In addition to the number cards that students already

---

*Ms. MacDonald was a field test teacher during the revision of *Investigations*. The accommodation *Build It,* which is described in this case, was successful not only with Linus but also with the range of students in Ms. MacDonald's classroom. As a result, the *Investigations* authors decided to incorporate this game into the revised curriculum. This case is an example of the power of teacher-designed accommodations and the partnership between teachers and curriculum writers in the development and use of this curriculum.

use in *Compare*, I gave students a Ten-Frame, which they would use to build the number, and chips. I chose chips because I wanted them to lay flat in the Ten-Frame to create a visual image of the number.

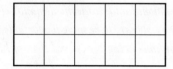

I gave the following directions for *Build It:*

- Player 1 turns over a card from the deck, establishes how many, and "builds" that same number on the Ten-Frame with chips.

- Both players need to agree that the number of chips matches, or is equal to, the number showing on the card.

- Once it is agreed the number was built correctly, the player ends his or her turn by removing all the chips from the Ten-Frame.

- Player 2 turns over a card and follows the same routine.

- Play continues until all the cards in the deck have been used.

As the students began to work with this new setup, I was delighted by how quickly they responded. I circled the room to see how the ideas were being established. Everyone seemed right on task. Then I turned my attention to Linus.

Linus was paired with Amy. I could tell that she was already frustrated because he would not take his turn.

Amy: Linus, you need to build the number. [Linus had turned over the first card, showing a 6.]

Linus did not respond. Was he waiting for her to turn over a second card as in the original *Compare* game? I watched for a few seconds.

Amy: Linus, take 6 chips and put them on the Ten-Frame.

Linus still did not respond. At this juncture I decided to intervene.

Teacher: Whose turn is it?

Amy: Linus won't play.

Linus: It's your turn.

Teacher: Can either of you tell me how to play this new game?

Amy: Linus needs to take 6 and put them on the Ten-Frame.

As Amy spoke, I noticed that Linus had looked away.

Teacher: Linus, let's try that. Can you take 6 chips and put them on the Ten-Frame?

Linus: Okay.

With this he counted out 6 chips and placed them in a pile on his Ten-Frame (rather than laying them flat as students were instructed to do). I could tell that Amy wanted to correct him, but I tried to interject before she could.

Teacher: How do you know there are 6?

Linus: I counted them.

Teacher: Is it easy to see that when they are all piled up?

Linus started to recount his chips.

Teacher: Can you show me another way to put them on the Ten-Frame so that it is easier to see? Can you put one chip in each box?

Linus complied. His Ten-Frame looked like this:

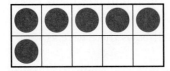

Amy turned over an 8 and carefully placed 8 chips on her Ten-Frame. Her Ten-Frame looked like this.

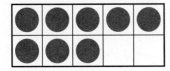

I watched as Linus turned over a 5 and placed 5 chips on his Ten-Frame. Amy then turned over a 9. As they continued to play, I was pleased to see that each student followed the routine and seemed to comprehend the concepts embedded in the game.

Two months into the school year, Linus is eager to participate in activities with which he feels comfortable. However, Ms. MacDonald's observation that he continues to hesitate when faced with new challenges results in a new activity designed to address his needs.

Questions for Discussion

1. What goals does Ms. MacDonald have in mind for Linus as he plays the new game *Build It?* How did she take into account both the mathematical ideas important for her students and the range of learning needs in her classroom?

2. After observing Linus play *Build It*, what might Ms. MacDonald's goal for Linus be for the next session of this game?

3. When you observe students struggling to understand a game, what do you take into account as you plan accommodations? Can you describe an instance in which this has happened?

It's Like a Cheer: Linus's Journey Continues

Although Ms. MacDonald's class of Kindergartners is now two weeks into the pattern unit, the work so far has been challenging for Linus. She has noticed that when Linus is asked to use cubes to make a repeating pattern, he snaps together random colors and is unable to begin a pattern on his own. She has also noticed that reading the patterns has been difficult for him. He often skips over a block or omits a section.

As this case begins, the class is discussing an AAB repeating pattern for the first time. The students seem to be comfortable with the shift from an AB pattern to an AAB pattern, except Linus who is fidgeting and looking uncomfortable.

Teacher: What comes next in this pattern?

Michelle: I think it will be yellow.

Robert: Amy said it was one color then the other color. That's this one [pointing to the AB pattern] but not this one [pointing to the AAB pattern].

I was ready to move on when Linus raised his hand.

Linus: It's like a cheer.

What did I hear? Was this the sound of Linus making a breakthrough?

Teacher: Linus, what do you mean, it's like a cheer?

Linus: It goes yellow, yellow, green [pause]; yellow, yellow, green [pause]; yellow, yellow, green [pause].

As Linus spoke, his voice was filled with gusto, and he even sat up on his knees and bounced a bit, much like a cheerleader. Did his vocalization and/or intonation help? Was it something about the rhythm? Was it a connection to something he knows more about outside of school? His mother often comments on how much he likes music.

Teacher: So by saying this part of the pattern [cupping my hands around one AAB unit], it's like a cheer you can say over and over. Does the cheer change?

Suzanne: No, but if you say yellow, green it changes. This would be a yellow, green, yellow, green cheer [pointing to the first pattern].

Needless to say, now our class often refers to the repeating unit of a pattern as a "cheer." It's taken on meaning and a life of its own. How exciting!

Ms. MacDonald noticed that the positive feedback Linus got from his classmates and from her helped to boost his confidence and seemed to spark his interest in math. Just two days after the pattern conversation, Linus was working on counting. For this activity, Ms. MacDonald placed three green bows, three gold bows, and three red bows in the counting jar. As Linus dumped out the bows, Ms. MacDonald heard him say, "Look, it's like a pattern."

Teacher: What do you mean it's *like* a pattern?

Linus: See green, red, gold; green, red, gold; green, red, gold [organizing the nine bows into an ABC pattern as he talked].

Teacher: Does this pattern have a cheer?

Linus: Yup; green, red, gold.

Teacher: Does the pattern help you figure out how many bows there are?

Linus looked up with a blank stare. Had I jumped too quickly again? I asked him how many greens he had, and he was able to quickly answer 3. Linus was able to tell me how many gold and red bows there were as well.

Teacher: So how many do you have all together?

Linus looked at me with that confused look.

Linus: It's a pattern?

Teacher: Yes, you made a pattern of green, red, gold.

Linus: That's the cheer!

Teacher: Yes, green, red, gold is the cheer. How many bows do you have in your whole pattern?

Linus: 1, 2, 3, 4, 5, 6, 7, 8, 9. Nine bows!

In this case, we see Linus, a student who up until now has held back, come forward and offer an idea that illuminates a class discussion. Contributing to the mathematical community gives Linus a much-needed boost that seems to be helping him develop the confidence to move forward with his mathematical thinking.

Questions for Discussion

1. How did Ms. MacDonald extend Linus's observation about patterns to build his understanding of numbers?

2. Ms. MacDonald could have missed an opportunity to further Linus's thinking and to bring his idea to the class. Can you think of a time when a student said something unexpected that at first glance seemed unrelated to the mathematics at hand? What did you do?

Change It: How Students Adapt Activities

Teachers often make accommodations to help individual learners in their classrooms. Many times teachers discover that an accommodation made for one student benefits other students in the class as well. In a previous case, Kindergarten teacher Samantha MacDonald created an accommodation to help one student (see "Linus: Building Numbers Greater Than 4"). She found that several other students benefited from more experience recognizing and representing numbers. In this case, two of her students create their own accommodation and, consequently, make even deeper mathematical connections.

After observing one of my struggling students play the game *Compare* in a way that allowed his partner to do most of the thinking, I realized that I needed to create a new game that still focused on number recognition and establishing a quantity but removed the focus on comparison. I hoped that this new game, *Build It,* would encourage more active participation from all students when they returned to the game *Compare*. Although my purpose in designing this game was to help a particular struggling student, I felt other students could also benefit from this accommodation.

As my students began to play *Build It,* alternately turning over a number card and building the quantity on a Ten-Frame, I was delighted by how quickly they responded. I circled the room to see how the ideas were being established. Everyone seemed right on task. They seemed to easily adapt to the new game.

I stopped to watch Lucy and John playing. I noticed that after John had placed 6 chips on his Ten-Frame, he did not take them off. Instead, when Lucy turned over a card, she quickly adjusted the set to make the Ten-Frame show the 3 that she was to represent. She did this by removing 3 chips. I thought I heard her say, "3 and 3 is 6." Their play continued in this same fashion for several turns.

Teacher: Tell me about how you are playing this game.

Lucy: It's easier to just change some of the chips than starting over.

John: Yeah, you just put out more or take some away.

After watching and listening, I realized that Lucy and John had modified their own game to make it "easier" and, in fact, more mathematically interesting. After one student built a number, the next student changed it in some way to show a new quantity. It was exciting to see how fluidly they either added or took away chips. I decided that I wanted to give all the students in my class an opportunity to try out this new version. At the end of the session, I asked Lucy and John to demonstrate their idea to the class.

Once the other students saw this version, we decided we could have two different games, *Build It* and *Change It.* I am eager to see which students prefer to play *Build It* and which prefer *Change It.*

Teachers sometimes fear that by adapting activities to help learners having difficulty, they might end up neglecting the needs of the more advanced students in the room. In this case, Ms. MacDonald creates an activity that allows students to work at a pace where they feel comfortable and is pleased to see some students modify her new activity in a way that creates a new challenge.

Questions for Discussion

1. Lucy and John create a new version of the game *Build It.* What new ideas does the modified version, *Change It,* allow students to explore?

2. What accommodations have you or your students made to games or activities to provide support for students who need it and challenge for those ready to explore more advanced ideas?

How Many Students Are in Our Class?

All teachers are faced with the task of meeting the needs of a diverse group of learners. In the following case, Kindergarten teacher Meghan Mallon writes about how allowing students to share their mathematical thinking provides a challenge for some of the students in her classroom.

Every year, I have a few Kindergartners whose understanding of math is broader and deeper than that of most of their peers. They make interesting observations that give some of their classmates new ideas to think about.

One such student, Andrea, came up to me during snack time one day and said, "There are 7 kids at my table, and if we count around the table 3 times, we get 21." As there are 21 students in our class, this was an exciting and noteworthy discovery. I expressed delight and asked Andrea how she came to know this. She said, "Because we did it." I have no idea what made them try this count, how it started, or what the original intent was. Not wanting to forget her great thinking, I wrote her idea on a piece of scrap paper and told her we would think about this some more later on.

The next day, we started the Kindergarten data unit. The first Investigation is about how many students are in the class and how to represent that data. I started with the acknowledgment that everyone knows we have 21 Kindergartners. Then I asked my students to consider the many ways we might check to be sure. I got a delightful range of responses, with students suggesting we count many of the objects we have in our classroom, including themselves, the names on a class list, the nametags on the cubbies, the writing folders, the self-portraits, and the cubes on our class attendance stick.

I then asked how they could show a total of 21 Kindergartners. We talked about using objects and making paper and pencil representations. Andrea very excitedly raised her hand and said, "I'm going to do that thing from the other day! I'm going to show 7 kids in one spot 3 times!" She was so happy. I had her explain her discovery to the class. Another student, Kirby,

said that he was going to do that, too. Other Kindergartners then said how they might show the total, and off they went.

Even though I have a range of learners in my classroom, every one of them was able to make some sense of the math, and almost all of them were able to successfully represent the 21 students in our class.

Most of my students made 21 of something—either stick figures, dots, lines, rubber stamps, or dot stickers. Some of their representations show each person in the classroom (names or initials, or this is so-and-so, this is me, this is . . ., etc.). Some students showed boys and girls in a generic way, and some showed the students in the boy and girl subgroups. Alex made an AB pattern of footballs for boys and hearts for girls, which (gender stereotyping aside) worked fine as there are 11 boys and 10 girls.

There were a few representations that stood out and showed some higher-level thinking. Andrea's was one of them. I noticed Andrea was finished in about 2 minutes. Her paper showed 3 distinct sets of 7 circles, with coloring around each set. She also wrote "7, 7, 7, 21." So, for Andrea, the 3 groups of 7, the 7 taken 3 times, translated comfortably from 7 students each saying or having 3 numbers, to 3 groups of 7 students.

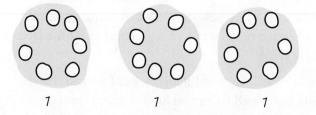

7   7   7   21

I said, "So you knew that since 7 kids counted 3 times, 3 groups of 7 kids would be 21 kids." She nodded. I said, "So if this was your snack table (pointing to one of her groups of 7 circles), and I gave you 21 cookies to share, how many would you each get?" "Three!" "Suppose I gave you each three pencils. How many would that be?" "Twenty-one!" It seems Andrea has put something together not only about 7, 3, and 21 but also perhaps about multiplication and division more generally.

Sam stamped 7 flowers across the top of his paper and then put 3 dot stickers underneath them. He said, indicating the stickers, "This means do these [now indicating the flowers] 3 times. "Wow," I said. I then noted, not meaning to be critical, that if someone walked in and looked at his paper without him explaining it, that they might think we had 10 kids because there were 10 objects on his paper. He paused and added an "X" to mean "times" between the flowers and the dot stickers.

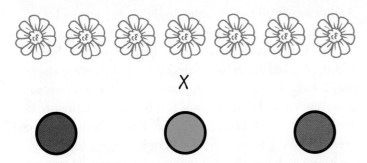

Walking away from the opening discussion, Kirby had said that he planned to draw 7 kids and write 3 numbers under each to show Andrea's idea. When I stopped by to see how he was doing, he showed me the following representation, dots to represent the 7 kids with 3 numbers under each dot:

•	•	•	•	•	•	•
1, 2, 3	4, 5, 6	7, 8, 9	10, 11, 12	13, 14, 15	16, 17, 18	19, 20, 21

I found that all of my students were engaged in this activity, including the ones who struggled with how to count out and make 21 dots or stick figures, those who were ready to include another level of information or organization, and those who were ready to think about 3 groups of 7 or 7 groups of 3. Representing the number of students in the class was an open-ended activity that students could enter in many ways and use to think about a range of mathematical ideas, from one-to-one correspondence to multiplication.

Andrea shared her idea, and some classmates picked up on it. I did not expect all of the students to be able to respond to her thinking, but her idea certainly pushed Sam and Kirby's thinking.

Is multiplication part of the Kindergarten curriculum? No. But are there students ready to think about it? Certainly! Will I "teach" more multiplication this year? Not formally, but I will tell some story problems that involve multiplication but that can also be solved by counting. I will look and listen for other signs of these ideas percolating in some of my students, and I will ask them what they are thinking.

In this case, Ms. Mallon demonstrates what happens when students are presented with a thoughtful, open-ended activity and plenty of time for student-to-student dialogue. Although she has a range of learners in her classroom, she found that all of her students were able to find some way to enter into and contribute to the mathematics happening in the classroom.

Questions for Discussion

1. **What was it about this activity that provided an entry point for a range of learners? How did Ms. Mallon respond to the needs of all of her learners while using Andrea's idea to also push the thinking of those students who were ready to engage with it?**

2. **Can you think of a time in your own classroom when a student shared an idea that some but not all students were ready to engage in? What did you do?**

Language and Representation

Sharing Marbles: Representing and Solving a Division Problem

Susan Sharrow's Kindergarten students have been working on addition and subtraction story problems. To prepare for a school-wide professional development day, Ms. Sharrow was asked to present her students with a division story problem. Although division is not part of the Kindergarten curriculum, Ms. Sharrow was interested in seeing if the range of students in her classroom would be able to apply the problem-solving strategies they had learned during the year to this new type of problem.

To prepare for a school-wide professional development day, all Kindergarten and first-grade teachers were asked to present a division problem to their classes. I gave my students the following problem:

How could 4 Kindergarten students share 12 marbles fairly?

I decided on this particular problem because lately my students had been manifesting a hard time sharing the limited supply of marbles we have in our classroom. I thought of starting with a smaller number of marbles to share, like 4 or 6, but I wanted the problem to reflect a real classroom scenario.

I found myself curious and interested about what the students might do to solve this new type of problem. Who would find a way into the problem and who would not? How would they use the marbles? Would they write or draw anything on the papers they were supplied with?

Just like when we prepare to solve addition and subtraction problems, I gathered the students together to make sure they understood the problem. I asked a few students to retell the story in their own words. Next, I had the students picture the situation in their minds. Finally, I asked them to describe the action of the problem and tried to help them pay particular attention to what was happening with the 4 students and the 12 marbles.

Satisfied that the students had a good understanding of the problem, I paired each student with a partner and sent each pair off with a cup containing 12 marbles. I was wondering how the students would do with this grouping arrangement. Although I was tempted to have them work in groups of four so they could act out the problem, I knew that 4 students in a group would not work in a Kindergarten setting. I couldn't wait to see how each pair would deal with the problem of dividing up marbles among 4 students.

Andrea recognized this problem right away. I was still distributing the materials when she said, "No one has 4 kids." I asked her if she could say more about that. She added, "Me and Sarah have only 2 kids, and everyone else has only 2 kids, so what are we supposed to do?" I sat down with them and noticed that each girl had 6 marbles in front of her. I asked if they could imagine 2 more Kindergartners coming over and asking for marbles. Sarah quickly responded, "Oh, we would each have 3." While she was answering, I noticed she split her pile of 6 marbles into two piles of 3 marbles. This small bit of using their imagination to visualize the problem seemed to really help Andrea and Sarah. They could imagine 2 students coming over and wanting their fair share of marbles, and they knew how to solve it right away.

Imagining the scenario seemed to help Mitch and Tom as well. When I arrived at their table, I noticed that they had arranged their 12 marbles into three piles of 4. Mitch said, "We only made piles for 3 kids. We don't have a pile for the fourth." I said, "But your piles have 4 . . . ," and he said, "But it's not enough for 4 kids." It seemed to me that he was pretty clear that he needed one more group but didn't have any marbles to make the fourth group. So I said, "Okay, I will be the third kid, and this is my pile. What if another student comes along and wants some marbles?" Tom quickly said, "We can each give her 1 marble." We each took 1 marble from our pile and created a fourth pile containing 3 marbles. I was surprised that Tom saw so quickly how to solve the problem, as he is a student who often has difficulty in math and has trouble counting.

Darlene and Anita were having a difficult time thinking about sharing among 4 kids with only two in the group. When I approached them, they had decided that 2 kids would each get 5 marbles and that there would be 2 left over. I tried to help them imagine two other generic students, but that did not help them make sense of the problem. I decided to do a little role-playing and began acting like a kid and pulled another student who was milling about into the group. I whined that it was not fair and that we wanted marbles, too. Darlene grinned and dealt the marbles out by ones.

Josie and Judith also dealt the marbles out to solve the problem. Josie said, "So we take 4 marbles out and leave the rest in." She then took 4 marbles out of the cup and spread them out on the table. I said, "Well, that looks fair but what about the rest of the marbles?" Judith dealt out another 4, putting one marble into each pile. Josie, delighted said, "Oh, there's 4 left!" and quickly dealt out a third marble to each pile. She then said, "Oh, we each get 3. Three, 3, 3, and 3 makes 12." While there was some dealing out by ones, it seemed that both of these girls were thinking about pulling out marbles in groups of 4.

When I asked Kirby how he solved it, he said, "It's 3 because 6 and 6 is 12 and 3 and 3 is 6." Simone added that if there were 4 kids, each pair would get 6, so each kid would get 3.

While this problem type was not familiar, I was really glad we worked on it today. The situation itself, sharing marbles, was near and dear to my students, and the mathematics was challenging, new, and interesting. I was so pleased by the way all of the pairs worked together, were able to make sense of the problem, came up with solutions, and were able to describe how they solved it. They were animated, excited, and proud of the work they did. I feel energized, and I can't wait to continue working on story problems about combining and separating.

This case illustrates what students can achieve when they have a strong mathematical background in problem solving. Although Ms. Sharrow's students had never solved a division story problem, they were able to use their previous experience solving addition and subtraction story problems, coupled with Ms. Sharrow's support of the range of learners, to approach a division situation with confidence.

Questions for Discussion

1. **What tools did Ms. Sharrow's students possess that enabled them to approach this new math with confidence? How did Ms. Sharrow encourage the students to use these tools when they were confused by the math?**

2. **Can you think of a time in your classroom when students were asked to solve a problem with unfamiliar content? What knowledge and strategies were they able to call on to solve this problem? What did you do in this situation to help them call on this knowledge?**

Reflections on *Collect 10 Together*

Meghan Mallon has been using Investigations *for over 10 years with her Kindergarten classes. During this time she has learned a great deal about the mathematics in which her students are involved and has developed specific strategies to support them in their growing understanding of math concepts. In this case, Ms. Mallon reflects on the activity* Collect 10 Together, *in which two players take turns rolling a dot cube, which has 1–3 dots on its various faces, to accumulate counters until they have 10. She recalls her past difficulties in "seeing" the mathematics inherent in this activity and shares how she needed to work through her own ideas about the mathematics involved in* Collect 10 Together *to make the game meaningful for her Kindergarten students.*

The use of *Collect 10 Together* has always been somewhat problematic for me in my classroom. I have always felt as though the math thinking in which students could be engaged was valuable and interesting. However, in my class *Collect 10 Together* was typically a game that students did quickly without ever counting higher than 3, figuring out their total, or thinking about how many they have left to reach the number 10. (Depending on what the students roll at the end, they may end up with exactly 10 counters or more than 10.) Thus, I felt as though there was not a great deal of math thinking going on.

I decided to clarify for myself the goals that I had for my students as they play *Collect 10 Together*. As I looked closely at the game, I concluded that the structure of the game provides an opportunity and encourages students to

- combine small numbers and to think about how far they are from 10.

- count on to figure out totals. Having lots of rolls that can either be a one or two pushes this idea of counting on. For instance, rolling a one encourages students to think about the next number in the counting sequence and the relationship between counting and adding.

- think about various big math ideas such as the commutative property (i.e., 2 + 3 and 3 + 2—both equaling 5) and using known facts such as doubles.

I was determined to look for all these math ideas as students played *Collect 10 Together*. Would I see counting by ones, counting on, or "just knowing?" Would students keep track of how many counters they had as they played or would they just keep accumulating counters without thinking about the total? What could I do to promote the type of math thinking that could be involved in this game? I realized that I needed to be more explicit with the students about my goals for the game.

During a class meeting, I told my students that I wanted them to play the game thoughtfully, and I explained what this meant. As I introduced the game, I was really specific about why we were playing it. In the demonstration game, I did not line the counters up in a neat row. I acknowledged that the game could be played very quickly and told them my expectation that they play again and again so they could do lots of counting and adding. Through the demonstration, I indicated that I did not want them to play quickly and without any counting or thinking. I also told students that I was interested in several things:

- How they played *Collect 10 Together*

- How they figured out how many counters they had

- How they figured out how many more counters were needed

The students gathered their dot cubes and counters. I had a clipboard and a sharp pencil, and we all went off to work. As I watched students play *Collect 10 Together,* I heard math conversations that were usually absent during this game. I was also able to prompt students to share their strategies and to work cooperatively with their partners.

As I looked at my notes, I began to think that *Collect 10 Together* is a game that can give Kindergartners a chance to work on counting and adding. It has the right number combinations built into it that allow them to begin counting on, adding, and using known facts.

I also think that if I, as the teacher, have a really clear idea about what the math in the activity is, I can then go after that in my explanations, teaching, conversations, and observations as I circulate. While it is important to be open to unexpected ideas that come from students, I also need to be clear about the math I want the students to think about.

It is important to continually reassess the mathematical goals of activities in light of the group of students with whom you work. In this case, Ms. Mallon shares her initial concerns about the mathematics involved in a particular activity that she has used with many groups of students. By reevaluating the goals of the game, her own goals, and the needs of her class, Ms. Mallon was able to present the activity in a way that made these goals explicit for students.

Questions for Discussion

1. How did Ms. Mallon focus students on the main mathematical ideas embedded in *Collect 10 Together*?

2. What questions can Ms. Mallon ask her students as they play *Collect 10 Together* to help them think about these mathematical ideas?

3. How might you apply this teaching strategy of reflection and redirection to a game your students know how to play but which is not moving their mathematical thinking forward?

"Heptagons" and Twins

In this case, Samantha MacDonald reflects on her students' work during the geometry unit, Make a Shape, Build a Block. *She finds that the mathematical ideas seem more tangible to her students than in other units and notices that even those learners who have struggled in the past seem comfortable working with geometry. She pays particular attention to her students' use of the new mathematical vocabulary they have learned and finds that despite their varying levels of discourse about the math, her students are able to understand each other and share ideas.*

Over the years I have noticed that all students have access to the ideas in this unit in a way that is not always true when learning other mathematical concepts. Though a student may not know the name of a particular shape or have previously differentiated the features of two-dimensional versus three-dimensional shapes, they all have had some experience

building and describing shapes. The students seem to pick up on the geometric vocabulary and are eager to give it a try. They may not always be accurate, but they get pretty excited about trying out new words. An example of this took place as a small group of students was working with the play dough we had made to support the work in this unit. I had added some cookie cutters to the basket of materials. One of the cutters was a six-pointed star. The students also had plastic knives and other modeling tools at their fingertips. As Norman and Sal worked, I heard the following exchange:

Norman: I see a heptagon in the star. Look I can cut off six triangles, and it's just like the yellow pattern block.

Sal: Can I try? I want to make a hexagon star, too.

Though Norman did not accurately pronounce "hexagon," it did not interfere with Sal's comprehension of his ideas. Norman passed the cutter to Sal, and Sal proceeded to roll out some dough, cut out the shape of the star and then cut off the six triangles. Their work looked like this:

Kim: Two hexagons and 12 triangles make 2 stars. Can I make one, too?

As we progressed from one Investigation to another, I never felt like I needed to modify the activities. This had not been the case with any other unit. Students who struggled with initial concepts in the pattern and number units did not struggle with geometry. Linus, for example, has been one student for whom I needed to make accommodations in most prior units, even if the accommodation was only to be close by and restate expectations/directions or to model ideas or provide a scaffold for his thinking. I did not feel I needed to do this for the tasks in this unit. Linus worked independently or with a partner. In particular, he really enjoyed building with the Geoblocks.

Linus: I found a twin.

Teacher: What do you mean?

Linus: This block and this block are the same.

Linus held up two cubes of the same size.

Teacher: Can you find other twins?

Linus proceeded to make matches of identical blocks. He seemed to generate his own activity as he tried to find all the "twins." His enthusiasm encouraged other nearby students to find "twins" as well. This spontaneous activity preceded the work in the unit of introducing *Build a Block*. It seemed only natural to jump ahead to this task and offer it as an alternative to his work. Before long, Linus was composing and decomposing the blocks with a fury. It was so exciting to see him take the lead. Earlier in the year he had coined the word *cheer* when we were working on identifying the unit of a repeating pattern. Now Linus and his classmates were in constant conversations about "twins." I couldn't resist jumping in as Linus and Lucy were talking about cubes.

Lucy: I made 2 cubes. One is just a cube, and one is 2 triangles.

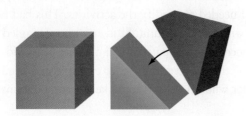

Linus: [handing Lucy an identical cube to her first block] This is a twin.

Teacher: Linus, can one "twin" be a cube made with one block and one "twin" a cube made of two triangular prisms?

Linus: You can make them look like a twin, but they aren't really.

Teacher: Why not?

Linus: 'Cause one and two are not twins. One and one is a twin.

Lucy: But they are both cubes. See. [Lucy proceeded to try and show Linus how the two triangular prisms made a cube.]

Linus: [again handing her the solid cube] No, you need one.

I was very intrigued with the way in which Linus was clarifying his definition of "twin." Though a shape could be composed of other shapes, it was not an exact match. It was exciting to hear his level of confidence, to see him take the lead, and to hold fast to his idea without wavering. This is a far cry from the little boy who wasn't sure how to count a set of 3 objects in September. I wonder if he would have generated the same ideas and voiced them in the same way had geometry been our first unit of the year. Was his access and success to the ideas in our geometry unit because of all that has come before, or was his success just the nature of learning about geometric ideas in Kindergarten?

As students represent geometric shapes in different media, they are describing features of the shapes, identifying similarities and differences of different shapes, and figuring out how one shape can be composed of other shapes. Students both use their own informal vocabulary and hear correct mathematical words for shapes used by the teacher.

Questions for Discussion

1. What mathematical ideas are the students working on in this case? How do students use models and language to communicate their ideas?

2. What lessons might Ms. MacDonald take from her students' experience with geometry, particularly students such as Linus who had struggled earlier in the year with basic number concepts? How might Linus's strength in geometry help him in other areas of the mathematics curriculum?

3. Have you had a similar experience with students who have struggled in other areas of the math curriculum but found new confidence and competence in the study of geometry? How have you used their strength with geometry to build their understanding of number and operations?

The Red One Doesn't Have a Match: A Counting Jar Discussion

Discussions are a critical component of mathematics instruction. In this case, Michelle Rutherford plans a discussion that enables her Kindergarten students to think about odd and even numbers. By asking her students for explanations and evidence to support their ideas and encouraging student-to-student talk, Ms. Rutherford facilitates a conversation in which the students are able to learn from each other.

Because of the cold weather this month, we have spent a lot of time talking about clothing that keeps us warm. Students have provided examples such as hats and mittens. I decided to incorporate the idea of mittens into the *Counting Jar* activity as a way to bring up the idea of odd and even numbers. To set up this experience, I found 6 pairs of gloves. I also found a single red glove. I put these items into the jar to give a total of 13 items for the students to consider.

As usual, toward the end of the lesson, I asked my students to come to the rug so they could share their thinking. The focus of the discussion was to confirm the total number of objects in the jar. I was also curious to see if any of the students might comment on the "odd" nature of the set I assembled.

Teacher: How many gloves are in the jar?

Many hands shot up immediately. I also heard students saying, "Thirteen." When I asked if everyone had counted 13 gloves, I saw many heads nod in agreement. I then asked the class why they all found the same total.

Steven: 'Cause there are 13. We all counted.

Teacher: Should we double-check?

Amy: I know it's 13, but we can count again, too.

I dumped the contents of the jar out onto the rug so all could see. Instantly Jason's hand shot up. I was delighted to see him take this initiative. It wasn't long ago that he sat at meeting time sucking his thumb, sat removed from the group, or fidgeted in his spot.

Jason: The red one doesn't have a match.

Teacher: What do you mean?

Jason: It is one.

Steven: Thirteen isn't equal.

Alan: It is odd.

Teacher: What do you mean?

Billie: Everyone has a match. No, not the red one [pointing to the single red glove].

Jason: Yeah, maybe someone took the other one to make a heart of a snowman. Maybe some animal took it. [Note: Jason's comments relate directly to two of the stories we had been discussing as a class during reading.]

Mitch: If we had another red glove, it would be equal.

Rob: Yeah, then we could count by twos and get 14.

Teacher: What do you mean count by twos?

Karen: Like 2, 4, 6, 8, 10.

Teacher: How will that help us with figuring out how many things are in the jar?

Rob: If I match them up (pointing to the gloves and mittens), they are two.

Teacher: Can you show us what you mean?

Rob carefully positioned each pair so that the two gloves in the pair were touching each other on the rug. He made sure to leave a space between each pairing.

Rob: Now you can count by twos.

Rob counted by twos until he got to 12.

Karen: See, 13 is not even. It doesn't have a match, so you can't count it by twos.

Rob: If we had one more red glove, it would make 14: 2, 4, 6, 8, 10, 12, 14!

Jason: But one is still missing, so we have 13!

By adding an "extra" glove to the jar, Ms. Rutherford creates for her students an experience that highlights ideas about odd and even numbers. To help her students probe their ideas more fully, she repeatedly asks them to explain their thinking and offer evidence for their ideas. Through this process, the students are encouraged to work together and are able to listen to and build on each other's ideas.

Questions for Discussion

1. What decisions did Ms. Rutherford make in planning this activity? What mathematical ideas did her students express during the discussion?

2. How did Ms. Rutherford's questions extend students' mathematical thinking about odd and even numbers?

3. How have you used a small variation in classroom activities such as the *Counting Jar* to extend students' mathematical thinking?

How Do You Draw the Ones That Are Gone? Showing the Action of a Subtraction Word Problem

In the following case, Susan Sharrow challenges her Kindergarten students to write their own story problems. She expects that most, if not all, of the students will write problems involving addition. When a few students decide to write a story problem about removing rather than combining, an interesting lesson emerges about the complexities of trying to show the action of a subtraction problem on paper.

My Kindergarten class had just finished the geometry unit. Before moving into the next unit, I decided to spend a little time thinking about numbers and computation with them. My class always liked acting out and solving story problems, but today I decided to add in a new challenge. I told them that they were going to make up their own story problem.

The majority of the students came up with an addition problem. They showed the two groups of objects with numerical labels and sometimes recorded the total. These problems felt like fine Kindergarten work to me; most of them were clear enough that I could tell from the student drawing what the basic story and action was in the problem.

The few students who decided to try a subtraction problem ran into some interesting issues about how to show the action of subtraction on their papers. Todd was the most expressive about the dilemma he faced. He handed me a paper that showed a jar with two granola bars inside.

I asked him to tell me the story behind the problem, and he said, "There were 4 granola bars in a jar and someone took 2 of them." I asked him how many were left, and he quickly responded with "Two." We both looked at the drawing of the 2 granola bars on his paper. We had the following exchange about his work.

Teacher: You know, I can see the 2 granola bars really clearly, but I can't see anything else that happened in your story.

Todd: I know; I didn't know how to draw it.

Teacher: What makes that tricky?

Todd: The other ones are gone.

Teacher: You mean the granola bars someone took?

Todd: Yeah.

Teacher: So do you feel like it doesn't make sense to draw them because they are gone? [He nodded.] Could you somehow add something to this picture to show that someone took some away?

Todd drew a hand reaching into the jar. He looked uncertain, so I pressed on.

Teacher: How might you show that the hand took 2 of the granola bars?

He drew 2 more granola bars, but now it looked like 4 in the jar.

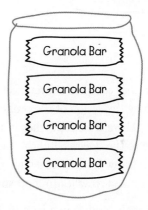

Suddenly, he got that light bulb being lit look and continued working on his picture with renewed energy. What Todd came up with was a hand superimposed over the top 2 granola bars, which showed the granola bars being taken away. Todd came up with a way to show the action of the problem quite nicely.

Judith made up two rather complex subtraction problems and found a way to show the action of the problem in her pictures. **Problem 1:** "There were 6 peaches in my basket. I ate one and gave one to the queen." Judith's picture showed 6 peaches, one with an arrow leading to a stick figure's mouth and another with an arrow leading off stage right.

Problem 2: "There were 3 candies in a jar and 3 candies in another jar. I moved 1 candy from one jar into the other jar, and there were 4." Her picture showed the moment when there were 2 candies in one jar and 3 in the other, and 1 candy in transit via a hand.

There were several other students who made up subtraction story problems. But as with Todd's work, the students all drew either the starting point or the end point of the problem without feeling any tension about the whole story not showing. I was very interested in how Judith showed the action in a subtraction story problem. I wondered what to do with this. Were the other students ready to think about subtraction stories and how to represent them on paper? I decided to have Judith and Todd share their papers at the end of math discussion.

A few days later, I made writing math story problems one of the math choices. I reminded the class about Judith and Todd's work and sketched Todd's hand taking candy and Judith's arrows showing peaches being eaten. I had not introduced the word *subtraction* yet, so I suggested that students might want to make up problems where something went away, left, got eaten, got bought, got taken out, flew away, turned into a butterfly, and so forth, and to think about how to show that going away part on their papers. Someone right away called out, "Yeah, you could cross them out."

This time there were many removal problems and about half of the students were able to clearly show the action of the problem. Their papers were filled with arrows, cross-outs, and giant hands (adorned with nail polish, rings, watches, and tattoos!) to show that something was being taken away. Kirby's new way of showing something leaving was to make a speech bubble coming out of its mouth saying, "Bye, bye."

After this work session, I am convinced that with a little exploration and conversation, Kindergartners can make sense of subtraction stories and that showing the problem on paper can help them better understand what is happening in the problem. I was also interested to see how the ideas presented by a few students could have an impact on the thinking of so many classmates.

Although Ms. Sharrow is surprised when some of her students show an interest in subtraction story problems, she encourages them to think through their difficulties and share what they learned with the rest of the class. As a result, Ms. Sharrow finds that many of her students are eager to try writing their own removal problems.

Questions for Discussion

1. Ms. Sharrow asks her students to create drawings of the story problems they are writing. What effect does this have on their understanding of the mathematics?

2. When Todd has trouble showing the action of his removal problem in his drawing, how does Ms. Sharrow help Todd work through his difficulty?

3. How does Ms. Sharrow's decision to have Todd and Judith share their problems and representations with the class help other students write and represent problems involving subtraction?

4. Have you made a similar decision in your classroom to have a student or students share an unfamiliar problem or representation? What was the result of your decision?

Helping Students Build on Each Other's Ideas

Meghan Mallon has spent a considerable amount of time this year teaching her Kindergarten students how to explain their thinking and how to listen to each other's ideas. In this case, we see how creating such a community of learners can enhance the mathematical environment and make even everyday classroom routines more thoughtful and challenging.

My students each have a counting collection. The collection, which consists of small objects found in the classroom, is kept in a resealable plastic bag. The number in the collection is supposed to match the number of objects in the counting jar that week.

For their morning job one day, I asked my students to count each other's collections. There were 21 candy hearts in the jar, so most of the bags contained 21 items. Not long into the activity, Simone came up to me and showed me a page she

had made. She explained that she had sorted Sam's tiles by color. She counted each color and then added them up. Her page showed 9 blue color tiles, 4 reds, 3 greens, and 5 yellows. By each line of color tiles she had written the number in that group. Across the top of the paper she had written 9 + 4 + 3 + 5 = 21. On this particular day we did not have much time to actually discuss the morning job, so I let Simone quickly show her paper, and we then moved on to our next activity.

Later that day, during math, I taught the students how to play *Double Compare*. In *Double Compare* each player lays out two number cards for each round, and the winner is the player whose cards total the highest number. We played a few rounds of the game as a class so the students could get a sense of how the game is played. I did not yet want to discuss strategies for adding or for figuring out who has the highest total. As I was gathering up the cards and getting ready to send the students off to play, Laurie threw out the comment, "Well, if one person gets 3 and 5 and the other person gets 5 and 3, it's still the same." The class had been sitting for a while and was getting restless so, as with Simone's idea, we didn't have time to discuss what Laurie had shared. I told Laurie to keep her eye out for that situation as she played.

After school that day, I had time to think more about Simone's idea. I decided to make a poster of her paper to show the students the next day.

The next morning I gathered the students on the rug and had Simone explain her paper one more time. We then counted the pictures of color tiles on her paper and on the poster and found that the total was 21, just like the 21 hearts in the counting jar. Next, we added up the numbers in Simone's number sentence 9 + 4 + 3 + 5 by counting on from 9 using our fingers and once again got 21 as the answer. I then showed the class a new collection of 4 red chips and 5 blue chips and said, "So, if Simone's way of showing Sam's collection makes sense to you, you might want to try to use her idea to help you count the chips and show how many there are in this collection."

Only two students can go to the counting jar at a time. Since I wanted more students to have a chance to think about this idea, I quickly made up trays with objects for the students to count. I put between 6 and 10 objects on each tray, and each collection had items with two different colors. As I did this, I narrated for the class what I was doing and thinking:

I'll put yellow and black cubes on this tray, and green and red bears on this tray. There—now lots of kids can think about counting the two colors separately and adding them up.

Before setting the students off to work with their collection, I asked Laurie to explain her idea about *Double Compare* to the class again. She used the same numbers, 5 and 3, in her explanation.

Teacher: So do you think this is something special about 5 and 3, or do you think this works with any two numbers?

Laurie: Any two numbers.

Teacher: So if I got 6 and 3 and my partner got 3 and 6, we'd have the same score?

Laurie: Yes.

I told the class that if what Laurie said made sense to them, they should be on the lookout for times when they had the same numbers as their partners but in a different order and should see if they ended up with the same score. And off they went.

I observed my students closely as they worked. Many of them counted the objects they were working with by sorting them by color, counting the items in each group, and then combining the groups. I observed some students using known addition facts to combine their groups. I also saw students counting onto one group to find the total, and several students counting all of the objects in both groups to find the total. Their papers varied in how organized and clear they were. Some students included number sentences and others didn't, but everyone showed the two different subsets on their paper.

After the work time was over, we sat in the meeting area and looked at some of the papers. On most of the papers, students could see where each subset was and how many were in it and could see the total. When we got to Kirby's paper, I commented on the row of 9 squares across the top, 5 blue and 4 red. Kirby had also written the number 9 and his name in boxes underneath the top row. There was also a good deal of other marking on his paper, which didn't surprise me, as Kirby likes to draw paths through letters and words, color over things to show action, and write codes and abbreviations. I was about to move on when Kirby said, "But I did Laurie's thing, too." I looked, and one of his rows of boxes also had 9 colored in—4 reds first and then 5 blues. I asked Kirby to explain, and he said, "Like Laurie said, you can do it in either order, and it's the same." I was very impressed with the connection Kirby made between the two ideas with which we started our math class.

We've had many conversations about showing our ideas and answers on paper; Simone spontaneously and independently applied this to a situation where it wasn't required of her to communicate a new idea about the counting jar. Students had shown the color of the items in the jar before, but there had not been any conversation about counting up subsets and adding them to find the total. Simone knew from experience that ideas like this should be shared with the class. Laurie expressed her idea about combining numbers in *Double*

Compare spontaneously and comfortably. The class as a whole listened to these ideas and continued to make sense of them as they did their math work. And Kirby connected the two ideas.

When two students make interesting mathematical observations, Ms. Mallon goes beyond just having the students share their thinking with the class; she encourages the class to experiment with the ideas themselves and provides a situation in which they can do so.

Questions for Discussion

1. In what way does Ms. Mallon show her students that their ideas have value? How does she give students who are ready to think about the challenging math ideas raised by Simone and Laurie a chance to explore them without overwhelming the students who may not be ready to grapple with these ideas?

2. Can you think of a time in your own classroom when you were faced with a similar situation? What decision did you make about bringing the ideas of your students to the class as a whole? What was the outcome of your decision?

Scope and Sequence

The strands are divided into Math Emphases.

The Math Emphases may be covered in one or more units. The Math Emphases are further subdivided into Math Focus Points.

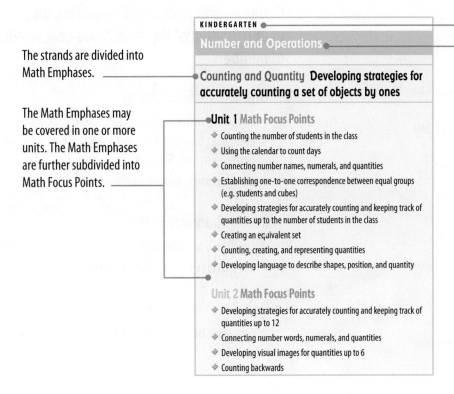

KINDERGARTEN

Number and Operations

Each strand is labeled with a grade level.

The content is organized around five strands.

Counting and Quantity Developing strategies for accurately counting a set of objects by ones

Unit 1 Math Focus Points
- Counting the number of students in the class
- Using the calendar to count days
- Connecting number names, numerals, and quantities
- Establishing one-to-one correspondence between equal groups (e.g. students and cubes)
- Developing strategies for accurately counting and keeping track of quantities up to the number of students in the class
- Creating an equivalent set
- Counting, creating, and representing quantities
- Developing language to describe shapes, position, and quantity

Unit 2 Math Focus Points
- Developing strategies for accurately counting and keeping track of quantities up to 12
- Connecting number words, numerals, and quantities
- Developing visual images for quantities up to 6
- Counting backwards

Number and Operations

Counting and Quantity Developing strategies for accurately counting a set of objects by ones

Unit 1 Math Focus Points
- Counting the number of students in the class
- Using the calendar to count days
- Connecting number names, numerals, and quantities
- Establishing one-to-one correspondence between equal groups (e.g., students and cubes)
- Developing strategies for accurately counting and keeping track of quantities up to the number of students in the class
- Creating an equivalent set
- Counting, creating, and representing quantities

Unit 2 Math Focus Points
- Developing strategies for accurately counting and keeping track of quantities up to 12
- Connecting number words, numerals, and quantities
- Developing visual images for quantities up to 6
- Counting backwards

Unit 3 Math Focus Points
- Counting, creating, and representing quantities
- Counting 12 objects

Unit 4 Math Focus Points
- Counting a set of objects and creating an equivalent set
- Connecting number words, numerals, and quantities
- Keeping track of a growing set of objects
- Counting spaces and moving on a game board
- Creating a set of a given size
- Developing and analyzing visual images for quantities up to 10

Unit 6 Math Focus Points
- Developing and analyzing visual images for quantities up to 10
- Developing strategies for accurately counting and keeping track of quantities up to 20
- Using subsets to count a set of objects
- Counting spaces and moving on a game board

Unit 7 Math Focus Points
- Counting and keeping track of quantities
- Matching sets with a 1–to–1 correspondence
- Working with 2–to–1 correspondence
- Counting by groups of 2

Counting and Quantity Developing an understanding of the magnitude and position of numbers

Unit 2 Math Focus Points
- Comparing two (or more) quantities to determine which is more
- Developing language for comparing quantities (more, greater, less, fewer, most, least, fewest, same, and equal to)
- Ordering quantities from least to most

Unit 4 Math Focus Points
- Developing an understanding of more than and fewer than
- Comparing two quantities to determine which is more

Unit 7 Math Focus Point
- Comparing two quantities to determine which is more

Counting and Quantity Developing the idea of equivalence

Unit 2 Math Focus Points

◆ Creating an equivalent set

◆ Considering whether order matters when you count

Unit 6 Math Focus Points

◆ Creating an equivalent set

◆ Counting and comparing quantities to 20 to determine which is more

Whole Number Operations Using manipulatives, drawings, tools, and notation to show strategies and solutions

Unit 1 Math Focus Points

◆ Exploring math manipulatives, and their attributes

◆ Using the calendar as a tool for keeping track of time and events

◆ Representing quantities with pictures, numbers, objects, and/or words

Unit 2 Math Focus Points

◆ Representing quantities with pictures, numbers, objects, and/or words

◆ Using numerals to represent quantities

◆ Using a Ten-Frame to develop visual images of quantities up to 10

Unit 4 Math Focus Points

◆ Recording measurements with pictures, numbers, and/or words

◆ Using numbers to represent quantities and to record how many

◆ Using a Ten-Frame to develop visual images of quantities up to 10

◆ Recording an arrangement of a quantity

Unit 6 Math Focus Points

◆ Using numbers, and/or addition notation, to describe arrangements of objects, to record how many, and to represent an addition situation

◆ Using numbers, pictures, and/or words to represent a quantity or measurement, or a solution to a problem

Whole Number Operations Making sense of and developing strategies to solve addition and subtraction problems with small numbers

Unit 4 Math Focus Points

◆ Finding the total after a small amount (1, 2, 3) is added to a set of up to 7

◆ Combining two amounts

◆ Modeling the action of combining and separating situations

◆ Separating one amount from another

◆ Adding or subtracting one to/from numbers up to 10

◆ Adding to or subtracting from one quantity to make another quantity

◆ Decomposing numbers in different ways

◆ Exploring combinations of a number (e.g., 6 is 3 and 3 and also 5 and 1)

◆ Thinking strategically about moves on a gameboard

Unit 6 Math Focus Points

◆ Decomposing numbers in different ways

◆ Finding the total after 1, 2, or 3 is added to, or subtracted from, a set

◆ Combining single-digit numbers, with totals to 20

◆ Modeling the action of combining and separating situations

◆ Separating one amount from another

◆ Developing strategies for solving addition and subtraction story problems

◆ Finding combinations of a five and six

- Considering combinations of a number (e.g., 6 is 3 and 3 and also 5 and 1)
- Beginning to recognize that some problems have more than one solution
- Thinking strategically about moves on a gameboard

Patterns and Functions

Repeating Patterns Constructing, describing, and extending repeating patterns

Unit 3 Math Focus Points

- Copying, constructing, comparing, describing, and recording repeating patterns
- Determining what comes next in a repeating pattern
- Comparing repeating and non-repeating arrangements
- Distinguishing between patterns and nonpatterns
- Constructing a variety of patterns using the same elements
- Comparing different kinds of patterns

Repeating Patterns Identifying the unit of a repeating pattern

Unit 3 Math Focus Points

- Identifying the unit of a repeating pattern
- Counting the number of units in a repeating pattern
- Extending a repeating pattern by adding on units to the pattern

Data Analysis

Data Analysis Sorting and classifying

Unit 1 Math Focus Points

- Identifying attributes (e.g. color, size, and shape) and developing language to describe them
- Comparing how objects are the same and different
- Finding objects that share one attribute
- Using attributes to sort a group of objects

Unit 3 Math Focus Points

- Finding objects that share one attribute
- Using attributes to sort a group of objects
- Comparing how objects are the same and different
- Observing and describing
- Using information to figure out what is missing

Unit 7 Math Focus Points

- Identifying the attributes of an object
- Identifying an attribute that is common to several objects
- Comparing how objects are the same and different
- Using attributes to sort a set of objects
- Grouping data into categories based on similar attributes
- Sorting a set of objects or data in different ways

Data Analysis Carrying out a data investigation

Unit 1 Math Focus Points

- Collecting and keeping track of survey data
- Describing and comparing the number of pieces of data in each category
- Interpreting results to a data investigation

Unit 7 Math Focus Points

- Choosing a survey question with two possible responses
- Collecting and keeping track of survey data
- Interpreting results of a data investigation
- Using data to solve a problem

Data Analysis Representing data

Unit 7 Math Focus Points

- Making a representation of a set of data
- Seeing the 1-to-1 correspondence between a set of data and a representation of this data

Geometry

Features of Shape Describing, identifying, comparing and sorting two- and three-dimensional shapes

Unit 1 Math Focus Point

- Developing language to describe shapes, position, and quantity

Unit 5 Math Focus Points

- Developing language to describe and compare 2-D and 3-D shapes and their attributes
- Relating 2-D and 3-D shapes to real-world objects
- Describing the attributes of circles and rectangles
- Describing the attributes of triangles and squares
- Exploring relationships among pattern block shapes
- Comparing the faces of different 3-D shapes and the faces of a single 3-D shape
- Exploring materials
- Relating 3-D objects to 2-D pictures of 3-D shapes

- Matching a 3-D block to a 2-D outline of one of the block faces
- Exploring Geoblocks and their attributes

Features of Shape Composing and decomposing two- and three- dimensional shapes

Unit 5 Math Focus Points

- Constructing 2-D shapes
- Finding combinations of shapes that fill an area
- Constructing 3-D shapes
- Combining 3-D shapes to make a given 3-D shapes

Measurement

Linear Measurement Understanding length

Unit 2 Math Focus Points

- Directly comparing two objects to determine which is longer
- Sorting objects into two categories, according to length
- Developing language to describe and compare lengths (long, longer than, short, shorter than, the same, equal to)

Linear Measurement Understanding length and using linear units

Unit 4 Math Focus Points

- Understanding what length is
- Identifying the longest dimension of an object
- Comparing lengths of different objects
- Repeating multiple nonstandard units to quantify length
- Developing strategies for measuring the length of an object

Unit 6 Math Focus Point

◆ Repeating multiple nonstandard units to quantify length

Classroom Routines

Today's Question

Units 2–7 Math Focus Points

◆ Collecting, counting, representing, describing, and comparing data

Patterns on the Pocket Chart

Units 3–7 Math Focus Points

◆ Determining what comes next in a repeating pattern
◆ Describing repeating patterns

Calendar

Units 1–7 Math Focus Points

◆ Using the calendar as a tool for keeping track of time
◆ Developing strategies for counting accurately

Attendance

Units 1–7 Math Focus Points

◆ Developing strategies for counting accurately
◆ Considering whether order matters when you count
◆ Comparing quantities
◆ Counting forward and backward

GRADE 1

Number and Operations

Counting and Quantity Developing an understanding of the magnitude and position of numbers

Unit 1 Math Focus Points

◆ Ordering a set of numbers and quantities up to 12
◆ Comparing two quantities up to 20 to see which is larger
◆ Developing an understanding of how the quantities in the counting sequence are related: each number is 1 more or 1 less than the number before or after it

Unit 6 Math Focus Points

◆ Reasoning about more, less, and equal amounts
◆ Finding a solution that fits several clues

Counting and Quantity Developing strategies for accurately counting a set of objects by ones and by groups

Unit 1 Math Focus Points

◆ Counting a set of up to 20 objects by 1s
◆ Practicing the rote counting sequence forward and backward, from 1 to 30
◆ Connecting number names and written numbers to the quantities they represent
◆ Developing and analyzing visual images for quantities up to 10

Unit 2 Math Focus Point

◆ Counting a set of objects

Unit 3 Math Focus Points

◆ Practicing the rote counting sequence forward and backward, starting from any number 1–60

◆ Developing and analyzing visual images for quantities

◆ Accurately counting a set of objects by ones, up to 60

◆ Practicing the oral counting sequence from 1 to 100

◆ Writing the sequence of numbers (as high as students know)

◆ Identifying and using patterns in the sequence of numbers to 100

Unit 6 Math Focus Point

◆ Developing strategies for counting and combining groups of dots

Unit 8 Math Focus Points

◆ Counting and keeping track of amounts up to 60

◆ Counting on from a known quantity

◆ Organizing objects to count them more efficiently

◆ Identifying and using patterns in the number sequence and on the 100 chart

◆ Identifying, reading, writing, and sequencing number to 100 and beyond

◆ Counting and combining things that come in groups of 1, 2, 4, 5, and 10

◆ Counting by 2s, 5s, and 10s

◆ Exploring a 2:1 (the number of hands in a group of people) and a 5:1 relationship (the number of fingers and hands in a group)

◆ Counting by numbers other than 1

◆ Developing strategies for organizing sets of objects so that they are easy to count and combine

◆ Developing meaning for counting by groups of ten

◆ Considering a 2-digit number as tens and ones

Number Composition Composing numbers up to 20 with two or more addends

Unit 1 Math Focus Points

◆ Finding and exploring relationships among combinations of numbers up to 10

◆ Recording combinations of two numbers that make a certain total

◆ Solving a problem with multiple solutions

◆ Solving a problem in which the total and one part are known

Unit 2 Math Focus Point

◆ Finding the sum of multiple addends

Unit 3 Math Focus Points

◆ Finding as many 2-addend combinations of a number as possible

◆ Finding and exploring relationships among combinations of numbers up to 15

◆ Solving a problem in which the total and one part are known

◆ Proving that all the possible combinations have been found

◆ Developing the strategy of counting on

Unit 6 Math Focus Points

◆ Developing fluency with the 2-addend combinations of 10

◆ Finding relationships among different combinations of numbers up to 20

◆ Using $5 + 5$ to reason about other combinations of 10

◆ Finding as many 2-addend combinations of a number as possible

◆ Trying to prove that all the possible 2-addend combinations of a number have been found

Unit 8 Math Focus Point

◆ Thinking about numbers to 20 in terms of how they relate to 10 (e.g., $10 +$ _____ or < 10)

Number Composition Representing numbers by using equivalent expressions

Unit 3 Math Focus Point

◆ Generating equivalent expressions for a number

Unit 6 Math Focus Point

◆ Generating equivalent expressions for a number

Unit 8 Math Focus Point

◆ Determining equivalent expressions for a given expression (e.g., $7 + 8 = 10 + \underline{\quad}$)

Whole Number Operations Making sense of and developing strategies to solve addition and subtraction problems with small numbers

Unit 1 Math Focus Points

◆ Visualizing and retelling the action in an addition situation

◆ Modeling the action of an addition problem with counters or drawings

◆ Finding the total of two or more quantities up to a total of 20 by counting all, counting on, or using number combinations

◆ Seeing that adding the same two numbers (e.g., 4 and 3) results in the same total, regardless of context (e.g., number cubes, cards, objects)

Unit 3 Math Focus Points

◆ Visualizing and retelling the action in addition and subtraction situations involving removal

◆ Estimating whether an amount is more or less than a given quantity

◆ Finding the total of two or more quantities up to a total of 20 by counting all, counting on, or using number combinations

◆ Modeling the action of an addition or subtraction (removal) problem with counters or drawings

◆ Developing counting on as a strategy for combining two numbers

◆ Subtracting one number from another, with initial totals of up to 12

◆ Developing strategies for solving addition and subtraction (removal) problems

◆ Seeing that subtracting the same two numbers (e.g., 6 from 10) results in the same difference regardless of context (e.g., number and dot cubes, cards, objects)

◆ Solving story problems about comparing lengths

Unit 6 Math Focus Points

◆ Solving related story problems

◆ Solving a problem in which the total and one part are known

◆ Adding 2 or more single-digit numbers

◆ Visualizing, retelling, and modeling the action in addition and subtraction (removal) situations

◆ Subtracting one number from another, with initial totals of up to 12

◆ Developing strategies for solving addition and subtraction story problems

◆ Solving addition and subtraction story problems

Unit 8 Math Focus Point

◆ Adding single-digit numbers

Unit 9 Math Focus Point

◆ Counting and adding to compare the distances of different paths

Whole Number Operations Using manipulatives, drawings, tools, and notation to show strategies and solutions

Unit 1 Math Focus Points

- Using the number line as a tool for counting
- Introducing standard notation for comparing quantities (greater than, less than, and equal to)
- Introducing and using standard notation (+ and =) to represent addition situations
- Recording a solution to a problem
- Representing number combinations with numbers, pictures, and/or words

Unit 3 Math Focus Points

- Using the number line as a tool for counting
- Connecting written numbers and standard notation ($>, <, +, -, =$) to the quantities and actions they represent
- Using numbers and standard notation ($>, <, +, -, =$) to record
- Recording solutions to a problem
- Using the equal sign to show equivalent expressions
- Developing methods for recording addition and subtraction (removal) strategies
- Seeing the 100 chart as a representation of the counting numbers to 100

Unit 6 Math Focus Points

- Using numbers and standard notation ($+, -, =$) to record
- Developing strategies for recording solutions to story problems

Unit 8 Math Focus Points

- Using addition notation ($+, =$) to record
- Recording strategies for counting and combining
- Considering notation for equivalent expressions (e.g., $7 + 8 = 10 + 5$)

Computational Fluency Knowing addition combinations of 10

Unit 8 Math Focus Points

- Developing fluency with the 2-addend combinations of 10
- Solving a problem in which the total (10) and one part are known

GRADE 1

Patterns and Functions

Repeating Patterns Constructing, describing, and extending repeating patterns

Unit 2 Math Focus Points

- Using a repeated unit to create a pattern
- Seeing how changing the unit affects the whole pattern

Unit 7 Math Focus Points

- Identifying what comes next in a repeating pattern
- Using the word *pattern* to describe some kind of regularity in a sequence

Repeating Patterns Identifying the unit of a repeating pattern

Unit 7 Math Focus Points

- Representing a repeating unit in more than one way (for example, representing a red–blue–red–blue cube pattern with the movements clap–slap knees–clap–slap knees)
- Comparing repeating and non-repeating sequences
- Describing a repeating pattern as a sequence built from a part that repeats over and over called the *unit*
- Identifying the unit of a repeating pattern
- Extending a repeating pattern by adding on units to the pattern

- Identifying what comes several steps beyond the visible part of a repeating pattern
- Comparing repeating patterns that have the same structure (for example, ABC), but different elements (for example, red–blue–green and yellow–orange–black)
- Comparing repeating patterns that have the same length of unit, but different structures (for example, red–blue–green and red–red–blue both have 3-element units)

Number Sequences **Constructing, describing, and extending number sequences with constant increments generated by various contexts**

Unit 7 Math Focus Points

- Associating counting numbers with elements of a repeating pattern
- Determining the element of a repeating pattern associated with a particular counting number
- Determining and describing the number sequence associated with one of the elements in the unit of a repeating pattern (e.g., the numbers associated with B in an AB pattern are 2, 4, 6, 8 . . .)
- Modeling a constant rate of increase with concrete materials
- Describing how a number sequence represents a situation with a constant rate of change
- Extending a number sequence associated with a situation with a constant rate of change
- Determining how and why the same number sequences can be generated by different contexts

Data Analysis

Data Analysis **Sorting and classifying**

Unit 4 Math Focus Points

- Describing attributes of objects
- Using attributes to sort a set of objects
- Looking carefully at a group of objects to determine how they have been sorted

Data Analysis **Representing data**

Unit 4 Math Focus Points

- Making a representation to communicate the results of a survey
- Making sense of data representations, including pictures, bar graphs, tallies, and Venn diagrams
- Comparing what different representations communicate about a set of data
- Using equations to show how the sum of the responses in each category equals the total responses collected
- Organizing data in numerical order

Data Analysis **Describing data**

Unit 4 Math Focus Points

- Describing and comparing the number of pieces of data in each category or at each value and interpreting what the data tell you about the group
- Understanding that the sum of the pieces of data in all the categories equals the number of people surveyed
- Using data to compare how two groups are similar or different

Data Analysis Designing and carrying out a data investigation

Unit 4 Math Focus Points

- Interpreting results of a data investigation
- Choosing a survey question
- Making a plan for gathering data
- Collecting and keeping track of survey data

GRADE 1

Geometry

Features of Shape Describing, identifying, and comparing two- and three-dimensional shapes

Unit 1 Math Focus Point

- Exploring the characteristics of cubes, pattern blocks, Geoblocks, and Power Polygons

Unit 2 Math Focus Points

- Identifying common attributes of a group of shapes
- Describing, comparing, and naming 2-D shapes
- Developing visual images of and language for describing 2-D shapes
- Recognizing that there are many types of quadrilaterals (e.g., rectangles, trapezoids, squares, rhombuses)
- Identifying and making triangles and quadrilaterals of different shapes and sizes
- Identifying characteristics of triangles and quadrilaterals
- Noticing shapes in the environment

Unit 9 Math Focus Points

- Developing vocabulary to describe 3-D shapes and their attributes
- Comparing size, shape, and orientation of objects
- Identifying the characteristics of 3-D objects by touch
- Describing a rectangular prism
- Comparing rectangular prisms
- Observing and describing characteristics of 3-D shapes
- Recognizing shapes in the world
- Describing 3-D structures
- Relating size and shape of an object to its use
- Planning a geometric structure with limited space and materials

Features of Shape Composing and decomposing two-dimensional shapes

Unit 2 Math Focus Points

- Covering a region without gaps or overlaps using multiple shapes
- Decomposing shapes in different ways
- Finding different combinations of shapes that fill the same area
- Seeing relationships between squares and triangles
- Altering designs to use more or fewer pieces to cover the same space
- Examining how shapes can be combined to make other shapes

Features of Shape Exploring the relationships between two- and three-dimensional shapes

Unit 9 Math Focus Points

- Matching a 3-D object to a 2-D outline of one of its faces
- Matching a 3-D object to a 2-D picture of the object
- Making 3-D objects out of 2-D pieces
- Making a 2-D representation of a 3-D object or structure
- Building a 3-D construction from a 2-D representation
- Visualizing and estimating the paces and turns required to follow a particular path
- Giving, following, and recording directions for following a path

GRADE 1

Measurement

Linear Measurement Understanding length

Unit 3 Math Focus Point

- Considering attributes that can be measured (e.g., length, perimeter, area)

Unit 5 Math Focus Points

- Understanding what length is and how it can be measured
- Measuring lengths using different-sized units
- Identifying the longest dimension of an object
- Comparing lengths to determine which is longer
- Identifying contexts in which measurement is used
- Understanding the meaning of at least in the context of linear measurement

Linear Measurement Using linear units

Unit 5 Math Focus Points

- Developing accurate measurement techniques
- Describing measurements that are in between whole numbers of units
- Understanding that measurements of the same length should be the same when they are measured twice or by different people using the same unit
- Understanding that measuring an object using different-lengths units will result in different measurements
- Measuring length by iterating a single unit

Linear Measurement Measuring with standard units

Unit 5 Math Focus Point

- Using inch tiles to measure objects in inches

GRADE 1

Classroom Routines

Start With/Get To

Units 1-8 Math Focus Points

- Connecting written numbers and number names
- Using the number line as a tool for counting
- Practicing the forward and backward counting sequences with numbers up to 100
- Counting by 5s and 10s

Morning Meeting

Units 1–9 Math Focus Points

- Developing strategies for counting accurately (Attendance, Calendar, Weather)
- Using the calendar as a tool for keeping track of time (Calendar)
- Developing vocabulary to talk about time (morning, noon, midday, afternoon, etc.) and sequence (first, next, last, before, after, etc.) (The Daily Schedule, Calendar)
- Collecting and recording data (Weather)
- Estimating quantities up to about 30
- Adding small amounts to or subtracting small amounts from a familiar number
- Investigating numbers that can (and cannot) be made into groups of two
- Naming and telling time to the hour on digital and analog clocks
- Associating times on the hour with daily events
- Counting, describing, and comparing data
- Making sense of a variety of representations of data

Quick Images

Units 1–6 and 8–9 Math Focus Points

- Developing and analyzing visual images for quantities up to 10
- Recreating an arrangement of objects
- Finding the total of two or more single-digit quantities
- Developing visual images of, and language for describing, 2-D shapes
- Identifying names and attributes of 2-D shapes
- Finding the total of two or more equals groups
- Identifying and naming coins
- Developing fluency with the addition combinations that make 10
- Using known combinations (i.e. combinations that make 10) to combine numbers
- Using standard notation $(+, -, =)$ to write equations

Tell a Story

Units 7–9 Math Focus Points

- Connecting standard notation $(+, -, =)$ to the actions and relationships they represent
- Creating a story problem for a given expression
- Developing strategies for adding and subtracting small numbers
- Solving related problems

Quick Surveys

Units 5–7 and 9 Math Focus Points

- Collecting, counting, representing, describing, and comparing data
- Interpreting different representations of data including: pictures, bar graphs, tallies and Venn diagrams

NCTM Curriculum Focal Points and Connections

The set of three curriculum focal points and related connections for mathematics in Kindergarten follow. These topics are the recommended content emphases for this grade level. It is essential that these focal points be addressed in contexts that promote problem solving, reasoning, communication, making connections, and designing and analyzing representations.

Kindergarten Curriculum Focal Points	Investigations Units
Number and Operations: **Representing, comparing, and ordering whole numbers and joining and separating sets** Children use numbers, including written numerals, to represent quantities and to solve quantitative problems, such as counting objects in a set, creating a set with a given number of objects, comparing and ordering sets or numerals by using both cardinal and ordinal meanings, and modeling simple joining and separating situations with objects. They choose, combine, and apply effective strategies for answering quantitative questions, including quickly recognizing the number in a small set, counting and producing sets of given sizes, counting the number in combined sets, and counting backward.	**Addressed in the work of:** • *Counting and Comparing* (Measurement and the Number System 1) • *Measuring and Counting* (Measurement and the Number System 2) • *How Many Do You Have?* (Addition, Subtraction, and the Number System) • Classroom Routine: *Attendance* **Also supported in the work of:** • *Who Is in School Today?* (Classroom Routines and Materials) • *What Comes Next?* (Patterns and Functions) • *Sorting and Surveys* (Data Analysis) • Classroom Routine: *Today's Question, Calendar*
Geometry: **Describing shapes and space** Children interpret the physical world with geometric ideas (e.g., shape, orientation, spatial relations) and describe it with corresponding vocabulary. They identify, name, and describe a variety of shapes, such as squares, triangles, circles, rectangles, (regular) hexagons, and (isosceles) trapezoids presented in a variety of ways (e.g., with different sizes or orientations), as well as such three-dimensional shapes as spheres, cubes, and cylinders. They use basic shapes and spatial reasoning to model objects in their environment and to construct more complex shapes.	**Addressed in the work of:** • *What Comes Next?* (Patterns and Functions) • *Make a Shape, Build a Block* (2D and 3D Geometry) • Technology: *Shapes Software* **Also supported in the work of:** • *Who Is in School Today?* (Classroom Routines and Materials)
Measurement: **Ordering objects by measurable attributes** Children use measurable attributes, such as length or weight, to solve problems by comparing and ordering objects. They compare the lengths of two objects both directly (by comparing them with each other) and indirectly (by comparing both with a third object), and they order several objects according to length.	**Addressed in the work of:** • *Counting and Comparing* (Measurement and the Number System 1) • *Measuring and Counting* (Measurement and the Number System 2) **Also supported in the work of:** • Technology: *Shapes* Software

Connections to the Focal Points	*Investigations* Units
Data Analysis: Children sort objects and use one or more attributes to solve problems. For example, they might sort solids that roll easily from those that do not. Or they might collect data and use counting to answer such questions as, "What is our favorite snack?" They re-sort objects by using new attributes (e.g., after sorting solids according to which ones roll, they might re-sort the solids according to which ones stack easily).	**Addressed in the work of:** • *Who Is in School Today?* (Classroom Routines and Materials) • *Sorting and Surveys* (Data Analysis) • Classroom Routine: *Today's Question* **Also supported in the work of:** • *Make a Shape, Build a Block* (2-D and 3-D Geometry)
Geometry: Children integrate their understandings of geometry, measurement, and number. For example, they understand, discuss, and create simple navigational directions (e.g., "Walk forward 10 steps, turn right, and walk forward 5 steps").	**Addressed in the work of:** • *Make a Shape, Build a Block* (2-D and 3-D Geometry) • Technology: *Shapes 2* Software **Also supported in the work of:** • *Counting and Comparing* (Measurement and the Number System 1) • *Measuring and Counting* (Measurement and the Number System 2)
Algebra: Children identify, duplicate, and extend simple number patterns and sequential and growing patterns (e.g., patterns made with shapes) as preparation for creating rules that describe relationships.	**Addressed in the work of:** • *What Comes Next?* (Patterns and Functions) • Classroom Routine: *Patterns on the Pocket Chart* **Also supported in the work of:** • *Sorting and Surveys* (Data Analysis)

PART 9

Kindergarten Math Terms and Index

Each entry is identified by the Curriculum Unit number (in yellow) and its page number(s).

Grade K Curriculum Units

U1 Who Is in School Today?
U2 Counting and Comparing
U3 What Comes Next?
U4 Measuring and Counting
U5 Make a Shape, Build a Block
U6 How Many Do You Have?
U7 Sorting and Surveys

Grade K Curriculum Units

U1 Who Is in School Today?
U2 Counting and Comparing
U3 What Comes Next?
U4 Measuring and Counting
U5 Make a Shape, Build a Block
U6 How Many Do You Have?
U7 Sorting and Surveys

Reasoning, U6: 174–175

Recording

addition, U4: 60–61, 62–63, 70, 74, 101–102, 110, 115, 118, 176–177

arrangements of 5 to 10, U6: 42, 45

combinations of 5, U6: 183

combinations of 6, U4: 131; U6: 36–37, 144–145, 148–149, 153–154, 156, 160–161

data, U1: 95–97; U7: 49–50

designs, U1: 128; U5: 46, 51

lengths, U4: 34–36, 39–40, 42, 46, 49–50, 63–64, 74

measurements, U6: 80–81

number composition, U4: 166–167

numbers, U1: 101–104, 108, 113, 117, 122–123, 142–143; U4: 77–79, 83–84, 98, 103, 139–141, 145, 154; U6: 101–103, 107–108, 113, 117, 121, 125, 130; U7: 35, 45–47, 51, 54–55

purpose of, U4: 15

quantities, U3: 37–38, 48, 62–64, 121, 127, 132–133; U5: 74–75, 78, 82, 114, 120; U6: 47–48, 71, 75–77, 92–94, 103, 108, 113–114

repeating patterns, U3: 71–73, 77–79, 83–84, 88, 91–92, 93, 97, 105, 135–137, 140, 145

separation problems, U6: 124–125

sets, U4: 36–37, 43, 46, 50, 83, 98, 103, 136–137, 141, 145, 151, 154; U7: 34, 47, 51–52, 54, 107–108, 112, 120

story problems, U6: 120, 122, 129–130, 131

strategies for, U3: 71–72, 78, 87–88

subtraction, U6: 116–117, 125

survey responses, U7: 109–110, 112–113, 132–134

three-dimensional shapes, U5: 95

units of repeating patterns, U3: 117–118, 120–121, 127, 130–131, 140, 145

Rectangles, U5: 23–25, 30–32, 37, 48, 135

Rectangular prisms, U1: 130–131; U5: 94–97, 109–110, 115, 143

Related problems, U4: 97, 103, 173–175; U6: 103–104, 111–112, 118, 171

Removal problems. *See also* Separating problems; Subtraction. U6: 116–117, 125

Repeating patterns

associating with counting numbers, U3: 16

body movement patterns, U3: 36–37, 41, 46, 59, 96, 144

comparing, U3: 48–49, 141–142, 145–146, 157–158

constructing, U3: 11, 42–43, 47, 59–62, 67–69, 73, 86–88, 92, 97, 105, 115–118, 120–122, 125–127, 131, 135–137, 139–140, 145, 153–154, 163–164

copying, U3: 36, 41, 46, 59, 86–88, 92, 96–97, 105

describing, U3: 11, 36–37, 41, 46, 48–49, 59, 71, 76, 81–82, 91–92, 97, 105

determining what comes next, U3: 11, 16–17, 36, 41, 44, 46, 49, 59, 71, 76, 81–82, 96, 105–107, 147–148, 161–162, 163–164

extending, U3: 11, 36–37, 41, 46, 59, 66–67, 71, 82, 96–97, 102, 104, 122, 139, 144, 161–162

identifying, U3: 10, 36–37, 41, 46, 59

identifying the unit of, U3: 11, 115–118, 120, 123, 125–127, 129, 131, 135–137, 141–142, 144–145, 147, 152–154

nonrepeating arrangements vs., U3: 41–44, 93–94, 141–142, 155–156, 159–160

one-two patterns, U3: 81–83, 88, 93, 97, 105

recording, U3: 11, 71–73, 83–84, 88, 91–92, 97, 105

sharing, U3: 106–107

Representations

characteristic of Kindergarteners, U7: 123–125

combinations of numbers, U6: 139–142, 152–154, 160–161, 179–181

of combining problems, U6: 120, 122

of data, U7: 26–30, 39–42, 51–52, 94, 116–117, 120–121, 126–127, 132–134

of increasing sets, U4: 61, 62–63, 70, 74

of numbers and quantities, U2: 12–13, 27–32, 36–37, 41, 48, 52, 59, 62, 63, 157–159, 164

purpose of, U4: 15

of quantities on paper, U1: 10, 12, 101–104, 108, 113, 117, 122–123, 142–143; U3: 37–38, 48, 63–64, 121, 127, 132–133

of repeating patterns, U3: 71–73, 77–79, 83–84, 88, 91–92, 93, 97, 105, 135–137, 140, 145

of sets, U2: 34, 41, 48, 66–70, 72, 86, 89, 92, 98, 119, 161; U6: 47–48, 57, 60, 71, 75–77, 92–94, 113–114; U7: 34, 47, 51–52, 54, 107–108, 120

of subtraction, U6: 124–125, 126–127

of unit of repeating pattern, U3: 117–118, 120–123, 127, 131, 140, 145

Rhombuses, U1: 128; U5: 23–25, 30, 37, 48, 70–72, 75, 83–84, 137

S

Same, U2: 12, 122

Saying one number for each object strategy, U1: 11, 87, 98, 135; U2: 10, 49–50, 73; U4: 75, 171; U6: 72, 166; U7: 10, 25

Scalene triangles, U5: 38

Separating problems. *See also* Subtraction. U6: 14, 18
   removing 1, U4: 101–102, 107, 110, 176–177
   with small numbers, U4: 90–94, 103, 107, 110, 114–115, 118, 137; U6: 116–117, 125
   story problems, U4: 13–14, 97–98, 103, 112, 137, 152, 172–175, 183; U6: 103, 111–112
   strategies for, U4: 97, 174–175

Sets, U2: 16; U4: 18–19

Shapes. *See also* Three-dimensional shapes; Two-dimensional shapes; *specific shape.* U5: 10–11

***Shapes* Software**
   classroom management, U5: 139
   composing/decomposing shapes, U5: 11
   Free Explore, U5: 34–37, 48, 52, 62, 119, 123, 126, 139–140
   introducing the software, U5: 11, 138
   mathematics in, U5: 141
   printing student work, U5: 140
   Quick Images , U5: 81–82, 100, 108, 114, 119, 123, 126, 130
   reference guide, U5: 34
   saving student work, U5: 37, 140
   Solving Puzzles, U5: 66–67, 75, 78, 83, 119, 123, 126

Short, U2: 160

Shorter, U2: 125–127, 160, 168–169

Shortest, U2: 131

Sides. *See* Faces of three-dimensional shapes.

Size, quantity and, U2: 63–64, 108–109, 111

Smaller, U2: 12, 108

Smallest, U2: 129

Solids. *See* Three-dimensional shapes; *specific type of three-dimensional shape.*

Sorting
   by attributes, U1: 13, 111–112, 117, 122, 136; U3: 10, 31, 33–34, 38, 48
   boxes, bottles, and cans, U7: 76–77, 78–80
   coats, U7: 141–142
   data, U7: 11, 92–95, 129–130
   people, U1: 107, 116, 121, 125; U7: 63–65
   repeating patterns, U3: 43
   self-portraits, U7: 67–68, 72, 78, 82, 87
   shapes, U7: 33–35, 47, 51

Special days, U1: 42, 44, 47, 58, 64, 82, 100, 110, 140

Spheres, U5: 93, 94–97, 109–110, 136, 150

Square prisms, U1: 130–131; U5: 143

Squares, U1: 128; U5: 23–25, 39, 48, 135, 137

Story contexts, U4: 172–173

Story problems
   acting it out, U4: 96–98, 103, 111–112, 137, 152, 182; U6: 14, 103–104, 111, 118, 120–121
   with addition, U4: 13–14, 96–98, 103, 111–112, 137, 152, 182; U6: 103–104, 111–112, 118, 120–122, 129–130, 172–173 174–175
   approaches to teaching, U4: 98
   comparing, U6: 104, 112,
   contexts of, U6: 170–171
   creating your own, U4: 172–173; U6: 170–171
   presentation of, U4: 174
   reasoning about operations, U4: 174–175, 183
   related problems, U6: 103–104, 111–112, 118, 171
   representations of solutions, U6: 14, 120–121, 124–125, 126–127
   strategies for, U4: 174, 182; U6: 103–104, 175
   structure of, U6: 171
   with subtraction, U4: 13–14, 96–98, 103, 111–112, 137, 152, 182; U6: 103–104, 111–112, 118, 124–125, 172–173, 174–175
   visualizing, U6: 14, 18, 103

Subtraction
   of 0, U6: 18–19
   of 1, U4: 14, 101–102, 107, 110, 115, 118, 176–177
   of 1, 2, or 3, U6: 84
   How many of each? problems, U6: 139–142, 152, 153–154, 156, 160–161, 180–182
   notation for, U6: 116
   related problems, U6: 111, 118
   relationship to addition, U4: 97, 103
   removal problems, U6: 124
   representations of, U6: 14, 126–127
   separating problems, U6: 103–104, 124–125
   with small numbers, U6: 116–117, 125
   story problems, U4: 13–14, 97–98, 103, 112, 137, 152, 172–175, 183; U6: 103–104, 111–112, 118, 124–125, 172–173, 174–175
   strategies for
      counting all, U4: 174; U6: 84, 116
      counting back, U4: 97, 174; U6: 103, 116, 175
      counting on, U6: 84
      counting on fingers, U6: 116
      counting what's left, U4: 97, 174
      "just knowing," U4: 97
      using addition combinations, U4: 174–175
   underlying assumption of, U6: 18

Survey questions, U1: 12, 95–97, 113–114

Surveys
   choosing questions for, U7: 12, 103, 104–105, 131
   interpreting data, U7: 112–113
   keeping track of responses, U7: 12, 104
   organizing results, U7: 11
   recording responses, U7: 109–110, 112, 132–134, 144–145
   sharing, U7: 112–113, 118

Symmetry, U1: 133

T

Tables
  of data, U7: 52
  of repeating patterns, U3: 16–17
Taller than, U2: 83, 168–169
Tally marks, U1: 142–143; U3: 64;
  U6: 122, 183
Three-dimensional shapes. *See also*
  Geoblocks; *specific type of three-*
  dimensional shape.
  attributes of, U5: 99–100
  comparing faces of different shapes,
    U5: 16, 114–115, 122
  comparing faces of same shapes,
    U5: 114–115, 122
  composing/decomposing,
    U5: 122–123, 126, 130, 134
  constructing, U5: 105, 106, 112–113,
    119, 123–124, 126, 130, 133
  describing, U5: 109–110
  developing language to describe
    and compare, U5: 130–131
  matching faces of different shapes,
    U5: 10, 107–108, 114–115, 124,
    126, 130
  matching faces to two-dimensional
    outlines, U5: 10, 117–118, 123,
    126, 130
  relating to real world objects,
    U5: 94, 109
Today's date, U1: 39, 120, 140
Trapezoids, U1: 128; U5: 70–72, 75,
  83–84, 137
Triangles, U1: 128
  attributes of, U5: 137
  classifying, U5: 135
  constructing, U5: 133
  describing attributes, U5: 37–39,
    133, 146
  equilateral, U5: 38
  isosceles, U5: 38
  relating to real world objects,
    U5: 23, 30, 37, 48
  relationship to other two-
    dimensional shapes, U5: 70–72,
    75, 83–84
  scalene, U5: 38
  types of, U5: 38

Triangular prisms, U1: 130–131;
  U5: 94, 109, 131, 143, 151
Triangular pyramids, U5: 136
Two-dimensional shapes. *See also*
  specific type of two-dimensional
  shape.
  attributes of, U5: 16, 135
  classifying, U5: 135
  combining, U5: 46, 47–48, 62, 65–67,
    72, 78, 83–84, 134
  compared to three-dimensional
    shapes, U5: 16
  composing/decomposing,
    U5: 70–72, 75, 78, 82–84, 134
  constructing, U5: 41–42, 45, 47, 51,
    62, 68, 133, 147–148
  describing attributes, U5: 30–32,
    37–39, 42–43, 147–148
  naming and classifying, U5: 135
  relating to real world objects,
    U5: 23–25, 30, 37, 48, 51, 59–62,
    78, 133, 145–146
  relationship of shapes to each other,
    U5: 70–72, 75, 78, 83–84

U

Units of measure, U4: 12
Units of repeating patterns
  creating a pattern from, U3: 139
  identifying, U3: 12, 16, 115–118,
    120–121, 122–123, 127, 130–131,
    142, 144, 145, 147, 152, 153–154
  relationship of size to quantity,
    U3: 141–142

V

Vertices, U5: 151

Grade K Curriculum Units

U1 Who Is in School Today?
U2 Counting and Comparing
U3 What Comes Next?
U4 Measuring and Counting
U5 Make a Shape, Build a Block
U6 How Many Do You Have?
U7 Sorting and Surveys

W

Weeks, U1: 38
Word patterns, U3: 36–37
Words, U7: 52
  representing combining/separating
    with, U6: 14, 75–77, 93–94
  representing sets with, U6: 94
Writing numbers, U2: 44–45, 48, 52,
  59, 62, 72, 152; U5: 95

Z

Zero, U2: 27, 102; U4: 144; U6: 18–19, 145